SPIRITS IN
THE VAULTS

© Tom Slemen 2011
Published by The Bluecoat Press, Liverpool
Book design by March Design, Liverpool
Printed by Martins the Printers, Berwick

ISBN 9781908457011

ACKNOWLEDGEMENTS

The author would like to thank Kevin Roach of the Liverpool
Records Office for his assistance in the researching of this book.

Tom Slemen

SPIRITS IN THE VAULTS

Liverpool's Haunted Pubs

THE BLUECOAT PRESS

Contents

INTRODUCTION

The British pub is dying a slow but sure death, possibly because of the rapid proliferation of off-licences offering their cheap drink, and also because of the rising crime rate; people just don't feel as safe in their local boozers as they used to in the past, especially in Liverpool, which has seen a surge in gun and knife crime in recent times. Then there are those economic recessions we keep having, and the price of a pint and a short keeps steadily climbing, so why bother?

Some sociologists believe the demise of the pub will ultimately be due to the ever-improving quality of home entertainment systems, such as cinema-scale multi-channel plasma TV screens with high-definition and three-dimensional vision and sound features. Why go down the pub to watch the match and buy drinks that are forever going up in price, when you can sit in the comfort of your own home, watching the same match or the latest film amongst family and friends and still enjoy the same drinks, but bought at off-licence prices? What's more, many pub-drinkers were also smokers, and when the national smoking ban came into force, pubs were forced to kick the smokers out, and now some of these die-hard nicotine addicts can be seen huddled in pub doorways or hidden in the pub's 'beer gardens', which are usually just backyards with the odd flower basket. This unfortunate but necessary alienation of the smoker has not helped pubs to sustain a regular clientele.

The pub has been near to extinction before, mind you, and still managed to recover. In the 1830s, the Railway

Age arrived, and the old stagecoaches which once transported travellers to rural inns became but ghosts of their former selves. The inns and public houses in the centre of communities managed to hang on, and with the arrival of the motor car in the early twentieth century, people once again fled the grey drabness of the city in pursuit of green open spaces – and, of course, rustic inns. The old coaching roads became busy once again, and the hospitality, for which our pubs and inns were renowned, became the order of the day again.

Of all the Saxon words in our language, the word inn has a welcoming warmth to it, and conjures up that bygone era when the weary traveller was welcomed by the landlord of a sleepy country tavern and furnished with food, drink, warmth and a place to rest for the night. The hospitality of the British innkeeper was always favourably remarked upon by the foreign traveller, but perhaps that heyday has now passed. Today, our travel taverns and pubs, with their plastic and neon fittings, fruit machines, giant plasma televisions and deafening juke box music, cannot compare with the open fires and thatched roofs of the old inns and public houses that once existed in the age of conversation. Can we ever turn back the clock to the days when darts, dominoes and table skittles were the only distractions in the pub? When the pub as we now know it goes the way of the dodo, the breweries and businessmen may be forced to reclaim the pub of old or face extinction.

This book is concerned with the supernatural goings-on in the pubs of Liverpool, and I have chosen those haunts of the drinker which, at the time of writing, are still open, so the reader can visit, and partake of the ale and spirits, if he or she so wishes. The drinks are on me

7

tonight. Grab your coat and let me take you out on the town, for the time has come for us to embark on a haunted pub crawl of those gutter drinking dens as well as high-brow establishments, which are to be found, not only in every area of the city, but in every era as well.

Let us forget about the cares of this modern Orwellian dystopia and set the controls of our time machine to much more interesting times, when people actually lived instead of merely existing. Let us desert the bland over-complicated computer-ruled world of today, and leave behind a sedated society which has as much character and rip-roaring romance as a plastic cup, and bid time past to return, so we may once again enjoy the sweet insane pleasure of green absinthe in the smoky gaslit dens of forgotten Liverpool, and become merry and intoxicated on the heady tales that were whispered long ago as parlour fires cheerily blazed.

Tom Slemen
2011

THE BEEHIVE
Paradise Street, Liverpool 1

The Last Laugh

The Beehive public house on Paradise Street is one of those rare drinking establishments with a warm and welcoming atmosphere lying behind the gilded affluence of its gold and maroon sign and faux-regency facade. The pub has a history that stretches back into the mid-nineteenth century, and was originally the site of a theatre, but long after the final curtain had descended on that playhouse, the comedy and drama continued to unfold on the premises, albeit in the unscripted plays of life among the drinkers of the new backdrop – a pub, opened by a victualler named Thomas Crump, who became the first landlord of the Beehive.

From the early 1860s to the late 1890s, the Beehive shared its premises with George Okell's showroom, which sold everything from household furniture to furs, stays and crinolines to table linen, ironmongery, bedsteads and Japanese goods. Crump and several temporary managers of the Beehive ran the pub until 1899, when a colourful character called George Tell arrived to participate in a ritual rarely seen in the pubs of today – 'the Change'. The Change marked the replacement of the former manager or manageress with the new landlord or landlady. He or she would go over the stock of the pub, peruse the licensing deeds, before an adjournment ceremony was held at the bar, where the regulars and former landlord or landlady gave a toast to the new boss of the pub. A notice detailing the change of hands was tacked up on the wall behind the bar, and the brass licensee plate was then removed from over the door of the pub and a newly engraved plate installed in its place.

George Tell was a much less stern man than crotchety old Tom Crump, and if the stories passed down are to be believed, he was something of an extremist practical joker too, who was responsible for all sorts of pranks and hoaxes. 'I do love jackanapery,' George would often remark. 'Mirth is the sugar of life.' There was, however, a rather dark side to the jovial jesting landlord. A rather scruffy down-at-heel prostitute in her fifties named Jemmy (short for Jemima) Rogers often frequented the Beehive, much to the annoyance of several self-righteous regulars. One evening she came into the pub, and George Tell greeted her with, 'Ah, Jemmy, a sailor friend of yours left this for you,' and as Jemmy squinted a puzzled look at the landlord, Tell retrieved a necklace from behind the counter and dangled it before his startled customer. All the drinkers smirked and watched, intrigued, suspecting that the landlord was up to one of his usual tricks.

You never could tell with George, he had that uncanny ability of keeping a poker face whilst perpetrating the most outlandish pranks. 'Who was this sailor then, cock?' Jemmy asked, and tried to take the necklace off Mr Tell, but he quickly withdrew it, then lifted the counter hatch and came out from behind the bar. He turned Jemmy around so she faced the mirror, and began to put the necklace on her. As he fidgeted with the clasp, Jemmy inspected the heart-shaped pendant and said, 'This looks like brass, cock, it ain't gold!'

'Don't you be ungrateful now,' said George Tell, fastening the clasp, 'that probably cost the poor sailor a lot of money that did.'

Jemmy turned and grinned, showing a blackened front tooth, and the poor soul, actually believing some sailor had a thing for her, asked George Tell to describe the seaman. 'Well, he had a patch on his eye, a wooden leg, and a hook where his left hand would have been,' George said, po-faced. 'Oh, and he also had a big green parrot on his shoulder, and that wore a patch as well, if my memory serves me right.'

The drinkers all started laughing, and then something very sinister took place. A whirring sound was being emitted from the heart-shaped pendant, and Jemmy held the vibrating heart and tried to get a better look at it, but a clockwork mechanism was operating a wound-up spring mechanism that was reeling the chain in, and the heart flipped out from between her finger and thumb as the chain was slowly dragged into the pendant.

In no time at all the chain began to slowly choke the

poor woman, and she desperately tried to pull it off, but the links were made of gold-plated steel. Soon, the chain had embedded itself into her neck, and her terror-stricken face turned a dark crimson colour. Drinkers jumped up from chairs and stools and tried to break the choking joke chain, but it was impossible without injuring Jemmy's neck, and she was now making a terrible rasping sound. Her tongue protruded and her eyes looked ready to bulge out of their sockets as ugly veins rose up on her face and neck.

Only George Tell still wore the traces of a smile as Jemmy Rogers collapsed. Two dockers caught her and took her outside as she slipped into unconsciousness. 'You idiot, George!' cried an elderly drinker, 'You've gone too far this time!'

Upon which, George Tell barred the old man on the spot.

After what seemed like an age, one of the dockers managed to snap the necklace chain, which left a livid red circumferential weal on Jemmy's neck. Slowly she regained consciousness and in a raspy voice she angrily promised Tell she would report him to the police. 'I'm sorry, Jemmy! I'll be having words with Mr Parry at his joke shop tomorrow!' George Tell cried in an earnest voice, and he dragged Jemmy into the pub and set a bottle of brandy down on the counter in front of her. 'This will fortify you, my lovely Jemima,' he said, but the prostitute started to cry as she felt the blood on her purple and black neck. The landlord told his barman to fetch a bandage from upstairs, and he bandaged Jemmy's neck and let her drink as much as she wanted all night, until she was arrested outside the pub for being drunk and disorderly.

On another occasion, a man in his forties, John Howard, began to frequent the Beehive, and the drinkers soon tired of his constant bragging. Howard claimed he had just married a beautiful rich young woman, whose wealth had recently trebled, because her mother, an infamous moneylender, had died. Every night without fail, John Howard would raise his glass and say, 'Happy is the man with a dead mother-in-law!'

Late one night at the Beehive, George Tell seemed intent on detaining John Howard at the pub, and even offered free drinks to the braggart as an enticement. 'I could listen to you all night, Mr Howard,' said Mr Tell, 'and to be quite honest, I envy you and your life.'

John Howard smiled in acknowledgement, and leaned back against the bar, basking in the landlord's kind and apparently sincere words.

'Hey, what's that smell in here, landlord?' he suddenly asked, sniffing the air.

'I don't smell anything, sir,' replied the landlord.

'Smells like rotten fish, or eggs that have gone off,' Howard told him with a grimace.

George Tell just shrugged his shoulders and set about cleaning some glasses. Presently he looked back at Howard and said, 'You know, I really envy your lucky life, Mr Howard. Didn't you say you were lucky because you'd married the daughter of a dead woman?'

John Howard giggled and shook his head, which set his body swaying. 'No, mishter Tell, I shaid, "Happy is the man with a dead mother-in-law" and my mother-in-law ish as dead as mutton!'

'Well if she's dead, what's she doing sitting over there then?' George Tell nodded at someone at a table behind the boastful drunken bore. John Howard shot a quizzical look at the landlord, turned around, and his eyes almost popped out of their sockets, because there, in the chair by the door of the empty parlour, sat the propped up body of his dead mother-in-law, still wearing her shroud.

The shock was so great that John Howard wet himself and also soiled his trousers. He backed away from the exhumed corpse and turned to the landlord, stuck for words. Now he knew only too well where that horrible smell was coming from.

George Tell wore a twisted grin, and looked demoniacally sinister by the thin yellow rays of the sole gaslight burning in the bar. 'Now, I think an apology is in order, don't you?' George snarled, and he leaped on to the counter, and jumped down, landing heavily on the carpeted floorboards beside the terrified Mr Howard, who let out a howling scream. George Tell clamped his broad hand over Howard's mouth and with his other hand, he roughly twisted the man's hand up his back before pushing him over on to the foul-smelling corpse. 'Kiss and make up!' the landlord cackled, and he took his hand away from John Howard's mouth before shoving his face into the decomposing, nose-less clay-like face of the malodorous cadaver.

John Howard fell to the floor, unconscious. When he came to, he found himself sitting in a dark passageway off Lord Street, caught in the glare of a policeman's bull's eye lantern. His filthy clothes were soaked with whiskey and stale urine. When he tried to tell the constable about his dead mother-in-law turning up at the Beehive, his story was not well-received, and he spent the rest of the night in the Dale Street Bridewell. When he woke up in his cell on the following morning, he had a chance to think through the whole ghastly incident. Could the whole thing have been born simply from the horrors of drink? For surely George Tell would never have resorted to hiring body-snatchers just to perpetrate the sickest joke in Christendom?

Despite his doubts, as soon as he was freed from the Bridewell after the payment of fines, John Howard visited the graveyard of St James's Church, off Upper Parliament Street, and saw to his horror that his mother-in-law's year-old grave had indeed been disturbed. Howard voiced his grim suspicions to the vicar of the church as well as to the police, but his claim was not believed or investigated in any way, and the vicar of St James simply advised Howard to stay away from drink and drinking dens in future.

Now we come to the next chapter in the dark history of Tell's pathological pranks and twisted tomfoolery. One rainy April afternoon in 1900, a prominently cross-eyed man with one-leg hobbled into the Beehive on crutches and asked for a glass of neat whiskey. After serving the man, George Tell turned to one of his barfly cronies and quipped, 'I thought he might have asked for a double,' referring rather distastefully to the double vision the stranger was probably accustomed to because of his crossed eyes.

Some of the drinkers laughed, especially when the afflicted stranger rested his crutch against the bar counter, took off his rain-soaked bowler and coat, and hopped on his one leg over to the table in the corner, where he draped the coat over the back of a chair and placed the bowler in the centre of the table. 'Reminds me of my childhood,' said Tell with a oblique smirk, 'when I loved to play hopscotch with my sister.'

The drinkers chuckled again, but then the stranger

15

came hopping back to the bar and picked up his glass of undiluted whiskey. He sipped it as a few of the drinkers, and George Tell, watched him with smiles of condescension on their faces.

'No one should mock the predicament of others,' said the stranger, 'for the Wheel of Fortune is spun by the Devil himself, and those at the top may become the ones at the bottom overnight, and the ones in the gutter may find themselves at the top of life.'

The smiles faded. The stranger continued. 'The plutocrat who tosses a coin in the street beggar's hat can soon find himself on the same pavement through so many unseen financial catastrophes. I once took my legs for granted. No one danced like me, or ran as fast, but a tangled rope took this leg off under the knee at the docks.'

'Can you still play football, or ride a bike?' a facetious George Tell asked, smirking at his cronies.

'No, I cannot,' the stranger replied, and threw back the rest of the whiskey in one gulp.

'Which eye is your good one?' Tell persisted, leaning forward and gazing into the stranger's eyes.

One of the drinkers spat out the beer he'd been drinking as he laughed out loud. The stranger tutted, shook his head, then hopped the short distance on his intact leg to fetch his hat and coat while everyone, including George Tell fell about laughing.

'You'll not stay for another one then, sir?' George Tell asked, pretending to scratch his nose so he could grin at the others behind his hand. The stranger said nothing, and left the Beehive. As soon as the door had closed behind the one-legged fellow, George Tell was already hopping about on one leg with his eyes deliberately crossed. The drinkers howled with laughter. 'The Wheel of Fortune spins round and round!' George said in a voice that sounded exactly like the stranger's as he hopped around the pub with his cross-eyed stare. One of the drinkers laughed so much, he fell on to a chair and begged George to stop, but the landlord wouldn't, until a policeman suddenly entered the pub with a cape glistening with April rain.

It was police sergeant Davy MacDonald, who was based at the Bridewell in Upper Essex Street. He had been investigating a local shopkeeper who had allegedly been receiving stolen goods, he told the landlord, but in the end the accusations proved to be baseless. The sergeant had been on his way back to the station when the heavens had opened, and so he thought he'd nip into the pub for a swift half.

'The usual, Mr MacDonald?' Tell queried, almost grovelling now before the much-feared policeman.

MacDonald was a fair man but very conscientious, and totally devoid of a sense of humour.

'Yes, the usual, Mr Tell,' the lawman said, and he parked himself on a stool, carefully took off his cape and placed it, along with his helmet, on the bar counter, as the landlord poured him half a glass of stout.

George Tell suddenly felt the strangest urge to imitate the one-legged cross-eyed man who had visited his premises earlier. He fought the urge, but was unable to deny the weird impulse. Sergeant MacDonald thinned his eyes, and beneath his walrus moustache, his lips turned down at the corners. 'What's wrong with your eyes, man?' he asked the landlord. The mouths of five drinkers who witnessed the audacious expression on Tells's face opened wide in awe. What on earth was the jokey publican playing at, gazing at the stern sergeant

17

like that? There was a time and a place for a joke, but this was just courting trouble.

'I'm really sorry Sergeant MacDonald,' said George, squeezing his eyes shut, 'it's ... erm ... eye strain.'

'Oh,' was all the sergeant could manage by way of reply, and his big hand reached for the small glass of stout and he began to gulp it while his dark, grave eyes remained fixed on George Tell's face.

'Let me hang your cape up for you, Mr MacDonald,' the landlord said, rubbing his eyes. He lifted the counter-flap, and picked up the wet cape. He then hopped across the floor of the pub in the same comical way he had when he had mocked the one-legged stranger.

'What the devil have you been drinking, Tell?' Sergeant MacDonald asked, rising from the stool.

Tell stopped hopping, and muttered, 'Oh, just a little joke we have among ourselves sergeant, sorry if it offends!'

Then one of the older drinkers suddenly crossed his eyes and said to the policeman, 'The Wheel of Fortune is spun by the Devil himself, and those at the top may become the ones at the bottom overnight, and the ones in the gutter may find themselves at the top of life!'

Sergeant MacDonald slowly put his glass of stout down on the counter and tried to make sense of the old man's words, but he couldn't make head or tail of them.

'What are you prattling on about, you old codger?' he said, wiping the line of stout froth from his heavy moustache.

Despite himself, George Tell started hopping back and forth on one leg, followed by two other drinkers, also hopping, and all three had their eyes crossed. The sergeant thought they were making fun of him for some reason and ordered them to stop, but then another drinker in the far corner came hopping over too. His left hand held his left foot up as he hopped vigorously about on his right leg. He too had crossed his eyes. The policeman grabbed the man by the collar of his shirt and shook him violently, but still the man continued hopping up and down the area in front of the bar. A butcher in his sixties came into the bar from the smoking saloon and asked the sergeant what was going on.

'They've been drinking something strong,' said an exasperated MacDonald, and with that he put on his helmet and headed for the door, leaving his cape behind. 'I'm going to get help!' he said.

They say the pub was closed for three days, and during that time the hysteria eventually died down, but it left George Tell a shambles. His reputation as a practical joker was well known and he was accused of spiking the ale for a prank; a prank that had misfired. However, it was soon discovered that none of the drinks had been tainted with anything.

Then a strange occurrence took place a month afterwards. The Beehive had returned to normality by then, but the landlord and the drinkers refused to even discuss the weird behavioural incidents, in case the phenomenon returned. Then, one rainy afternoon, a well-dressed man walked into the pub and asked for a neat whiskey. The landlord immediately recognised him as the man with the crossed eyes, despite the fact that his eyes were now perfectly aligned and, moreover, he now had two legs. George Tell suspected that one of the legs must be wooden and he challenged the stranger to show them. He calmly lifted his trousers to reveal two perfectly normal, though very pale, flesh and blood shins. According to legend, George Tell then said, 'So that leg isn't wooden? It's not false?'

'The leg's not false, but my face … well, you can see for yourself.'

At that he pinched his own chin with finger and thumb and lifted some kind of rubbery mask to reveal the hideous face of something that was surely only masquerading as a man; a devil perhaps. All of the drinkers recoiled in horror as the visitor pulled down this more acceptable 'face' over his demonic countenance. The stranger then downed the neat whiskey, then turned to George Tell and said, 'I'll be seeing you, George!' He then walked out of the pub and on to a rain-slicked Paradise Street.

As soon as he had left the premises the braver drinkers hurried to the doorway of the Beehive and looked out into one of Liverpool's most busy thoroughfares. There they saw the masked fiend skipping and dancing along in a heavy downpour until he turned the corner on to Church Street. He peeped his head around the corner a few seconds later, obviously knowing he was being watched, then tilted his hat at the frightened observers, and vanished for good.

Perhaps the fabled Wheel of Fortune was not kind to George Tell after that eventful day, because he eventually lost his pub, his health deteriorated, and he went steadily down in the world.

On his deathbed, he specifically requested a prominent Catholic canon to be present, and yet with bulging eyes, he still screamed at something that only he could see at the bottom of his bed as he parted from this world, bound for who knows where. Some believe the earthbound spirit of the mischievous former landlord still haunts the Beehive, for there have been many strange incidents at the pub that defy all rational explanation.

What follows is just a small percentage of the strange goings-on at this pub.

Gypsy Marie

People will resort to anything in an effort to see what the future holds. Seven days a week, every week, thousands of people pore over the newspaper horoscope columns to see what the Zodiac decrees, but there are other, much less safe methods of divination into the future. Here we all are in the twenty-first century, surely a modern era which has no room for ghosts and quaking quagmires of superstition? Well, surprisingly enough, science and the supernatural are now fusing into a one-world-view of existence.

While the high priests of subatomic physics are trying to unravel the mysteries of time and the universe with the Large Hadron Collider, people in the street are resorting to occultism to see what lies ahead in these turbulent times. Self-appointed mediums with the combined spiel of Arthur Daly and Del Trotter are consulted for often exorbitant fees, bewildering Tarot card readers are visited, and radio and television 'psychics' claim they have a hotline to the dead. Even the end-of-the-pier fortune tellers and their crystal balls are making a comeback in the Supernatural Renaissance, but I know from experience from having dealings with real mediums and real occultists, that the future is most definitely not always ours to see, and the following story, which took place in the Beehive pub, is a case in point.

In the late 1950s a woman named Marie, said to have been of real Romany Gypsy descent, frequented several pubs in the city centre, and for the price of half a crown, she would tell the drinkers' fortunes.

One of the pubs Marie frequented fairly regularly was the Beehive on Paradise Street. Unlike some fortune tellers and Tarot card readers, Marie was very specific in her forecasts, and news of her uncanny ability soon got round, and her reputation as a genuine psychic eventually reached the ears of a sceptical academic named Gerald at Liverpool University. Gerald was a professor of advanced mathematics, specialising in probability theory, the nearest science comes to prediction. Gerald went in search of Marie one weekend, and after searching several pubs for her, he finally found the alleged fortune teller in the Beehive on Paradise Street. The professor offered her ten shillings to have his fortune told. Marie refused, alleging that he had only come to her to try and catch her out and prove her to be a fraud.

Gerald then asked Marie to reveal three definite incidents which would be happening in the near future. Marie peered into her crystal ball for a long time, then solemnly raised her head and looked Gerald straight in the eye as she pronounced the most devastating prediction anyone can be given. Gerald, she said, would be dead within six months, at the end of June. To prove that she could see into the future, she also predicted a plane crash with a great loss of life that would take place locally in snowy conditions in one month's time. she also told him that she could clearly see the three legged symbol of the Isle of Man.

The sceptic returned her penetrating gaze and grinned as he asked about the second prediction. Without hesitation, the gypsy said that there would be another local plane crash, this time on the banks of the Mersey, in which a single man would die. This man would be known to a friend of Gerald's.

The learned man then triumphantly produced a small reel-to-reel Grundig tape recorder from his haversack and announced that he had captured all three of Marie's sham predictions tape. If they failed to come true, he would be sending the transcript of the recording to the offices of the *Liverpool Daily Post* and *Echo*. He seemed pretty pleased with himself and was confident that the grim forecast would amount to nothing but hot air.

That confidence turned out to be misplaced, because a month later, on 27 February 1958, 35 people died when their plane, a Bristol Wayfarer, owned by Silver City Airways, crashed into the side of Winter Hill, in Lancashire. There were seven survivors, but rescuers had to battle their way through heavy snowdrifts in order to reach the scene of the crash. The plane had flown from the Isle of Man. Marie had clearly seen the triskelion, the ancient three-legged symbol of the Isle of Man in her crystal ball vision.

The passing of the predicted event definitely made the university tutor a bit nervous but he tried to reassure himself that he was safe by dismissing the plane crash as mere coincidence.

Then, at the end of the following month, on 30 March, a two-seater Tiger Moth plane crashed into the muddy banks of the River Mersey, killing its pilot, 38-year-old aircraft instructor, Jack Green, of Queen's Drive, Liverpool. A friend of Gerald's knew this man. The other person in the crashed plane, a 32-year-old pupil, named Arthur Hobin, of Huyton, was rescued from the quicksand and rushing tide. The tail of the plane could be seen for hours, sticking of out the sandbanks of the River Mersey.

By now, our professor of advanced mathematics was becoming decidedly jittery, and fearing he just might drop dead after all, in the interests of scientific research he gave the recording of the interview to his friend, a man who worked as a journalist at the *Liverpool Daily Post* and *Echo*. In June of that year, the sceptical lecturer dropped dead while he was visiting his father in Cornwall. Though his heart was found to be perfectly healthy, the coroner had to record a verdict of death by natural causes.

Not long after the professor's death, Marie the gypsy vanished into obscurity. She said that her ability to see into the future seemed to be sharpened when she practised her dark arts in the Beehive for some reason, and when she was in that pub, she felt as if a man was standing over her, feeding her with all sorts of information.

THE COFFEE HOUSE
Church Road South, Wavertree

The Death Clock

If you need a reminder of the shortness of your life, look at a clock, and imagine if you will, that each five minutes measures a decade of your life. You are born at noon and, if you are lucky enough to reach the age of 75, which is currently the life-expectancy of we Westerners, then you'll be dead by the time the clock reaches half-past seven, and already it's probably later than you think. The clock is an attendant Grim Reaper, cutting us down, not with a scythe, but with its sweeping hands.

If ever a clock was synonymous with death and misfortune, I would say it was the Picton Clock which has surveyed Wavertree with its four faces since 1884, when Sir James Picton presented it to the locals as a memorial clock, dedicated to the memory of his late wife Sarah, who had passed away in 1879.

Over the years, a strange apparition has haunted one of the dials of this clockwork giant, a ghostly human face whose appearance supposedly heralds doom and misfortune. The earliest report I have of the spectral visage is from around 1954, when several people noticed that something looked 'wrong' with the western face of the Picton Clock – the one that looks directly down Wavertree High Street.

The time of this strange incident was around 9.15pm, when the clock faces were illuminated by dim orange lights, but the western dial seemed to have a series of blemishes upon it that slowly materialised into an eerie-looking four-foot-tall face with beady eyes. One old woman from Prince Alfred Road who witnessed the apparition, made the sign of the cross. She had seen the face before, she said, and had lost her young sister that same night from pneumonia.

About 20 seconds elapsed before the face on the golden translucent clock dial slowly vanished as mysteriously as it had appeared. On the following day, three young girls returning from the Magnet cinema, which stood a few hundreds yards from the Picton Clock, went to Wavertree High Street to buy sweets. With cheeks bulging with black jacks and gobstoppers, they then attempted to cross the busy road to go home, but the girls nearly choked when a taxi screeched to a halt just a few feet away from them. The cab driver shook his head at their carelessness, but he smiled and gestured for the girls to cross. They smiled back and started to cross, but a bus overtaking the taxi didn't see them and hit the third girl. She was pinned under the wheels of the bus and died from shock.

A fair number of the locals believed that the ghastly face which had appeared on the Picton Clock the night before had been some kind of omen warning of the tragedy.

About a month afterwards at midnight, teddy boy Frank Hokerift was returning from his girlfriend's house on Eastdale Road, on his way home to Childwall, when he too saw the spine-chilling face appear on the clock facing the Wavertree High Street. A car travelling up the street slowed, and the driver popped his head out of the vehicle's window to get a proper look, because he thought he was seeing things. He shouted to Frank, 'Hey mate, can you see that face up there?' Frank nodded and said he could. The driver swore with relief and said, 'Thank God for that, I thought I was going dool-alley. What the devil is it?' Late drinkers coming out of the Coffee House pub saw the face too, before it faded away a minute later.

Within an hour, a car had crashed near the very roundabout on which the clock stood, and the driver's body was thrown through the windscreen and landed with a sickening thud on the pavement outside Jenkins the undertakers, which still stands at this location near to the Coffee House public house.

Whose face haunts the Picton Clock? I cannot say. I heard a story many years ago from an old local man who maintained that a clock-mender decided to hang himself in the clock-tower many years ago, possibly in the 1920s, after becoming depressed following the death of his wife. Not long afterwards, his tormented face began to appear

27

on the dials of the clock and those who were unlucky enough to see the manifestations soon realised that the face foretold tragedy and death.

To date, I have been unable to find any reported suicides within the clock-tower, but sometimes such acts were not reported, out of respect for the victim's family, and suicide was, for many years, deemed a very unholy act.

Incidentally, I received a reported sighting of the spectral face in the clock-dial on the eve of the partial collapse of the nearby Lamb Hotel pub in August 2007.

The Wavertree Coat

The Coffee House pub dates back to the 1820s, and served as an ancient tavern in the days before the expansion of the city, when it out over the rural wilderness of Childwall. Farmers and villagers in those days would take refreshment in the Coffee House, and huntsmen would assemble on the common in front of the pub for their stirrup-cups. In those times, the Jordan Brook – originating from the Jordan River which flows from Otterspool – crossed Wavertree Road at Brook House Farm, from which the Brook House pub on Smithdown Road gets its name.

By the 1850s, the Coffee House was well established as a prominent coaching inn, as was its rival, the nearby Lamb Hotel, which dates back even earlier to 1754. From the 1870s to Edwardian times, the Crown Brewery was also incorporated into the Coffee House, which proved to be a very profitable idea during the winter months, when heavy snow often prevented the delivery of ale to the other inns of Wavertree. Many strange and wonderful incidents have unfolded within the walls of the Coffee House during its long life. I have detailed some of these in my books, namely, the story of the Wavertree Coat, documented in *Strange Liverpool*. This was the story of a bizarre challenge, issued in 1905, by one Thomas Tweddle, junior manager of the local bank, as he quaffed his ale in the Coffee House. Tweddle had been listening to the inane challenges that the drinkers of the pub had been setting one another, and so he announced: 'Now, gentleman, here is a real challenge, and I will pay three hundred pounds to the man who proves me wrong. This jacket I wear, is of the purest wool fibre. If any person here can make such a coat between sunrise and sunset on a summer's day, from wool freshly taken from the coat of sheep, I will pay him the sum of three hundred pounds.'

'Impossible!' the landlord of the Coffee House decided, but two of the drinkers were quick to take up the challenge. Farmer Jackson of Childwall provided two sheep and Isaac Nieman, a local sartorial wizard with the needle and thread, volunteered to be the tailor, and local headmaster Mr Gill, said he would enlist the help of relatives in Huyton who had old, but functional looms which could be used to spin the wool and weave it. Mr Aitken, the local chemist, enthusiastically joined in the challenge and promised to provide the black fabric dye for the coat.

Mr Tweddle, who issued the challenge, supervised all the proceedings to rule out trickery and things were progressing surprisingly well until the tailor, Mr Nieman, discovered that his shop had been broken into and most of his tools had been stolen. Fortunately a dressmaker named Mary Davies came to the rescue and not only lent her tools to Nieman, but also drafted in a number of relatives who were skilled at with a needle.

Between sunrise and sunset in that August of 1905, the Wavertree Coat was produced and proudly presented to Thomas Tweddle, who was forced to cough up the three hundred pounds, which was shared amongst all those who had participated in the creation of the garment.

The coat fitted Tweddle perfectly and it was exhibited as a talking point at the Coffee House until it was stolen during a break-in at the pub in 1910.

Time, Gentleman, Please!

In 1970, a Hunts Cross man named Reginald Scott visited his brother's flat in Wavertree Gardens, and afterwards called in at the Coffee House for 'a swift half' before making his way home.

That evening the pub was unusually quiet, with only a handful of drinkers scattered about the place. Mr Scott whistled as he waited patiently for the barmaid to serve his half-pint of mild. An old man in his late seventies stood by him, and the barmaid served the pensioner's beverage first: a pint of Guinness. The old man paid the barmaid, then rolled himself a cigarette as he waited for the Guinness to settle.

'That looks lovely,' said a voice which seemed to be coming from between Reginald Scott and the elderly drinker, startling the two of them, because they were the only drinkers in that part of the pub. Mr Scott turned around and saw a man in some sort of uniform standing there, eyeing the old man's pint of Guinness.

'Ooo, I wish I could sink that,' sighed the uniformed stranger, and shook his head gently as he smiled.

Before either of the men could reply, the stranger had

vanished, disappeared, right before their eyes. The pensioner tottered backwards in shock, but Mr Scott managed to grab him before he hit the floor. The barmaid leaned over the counter and looked down at the two men and asked what had happened.

'It was him again,' the old man told her, in between gasps as his hand clutched at his heart.

'Oh, was it really?' the barmaid replied, then looked at Mr Scott. 'It's a fellah in Walton,' she said, by way of explanation, but after that she seemed stuck for words.

'He ... he ... he just disappeared,' a wide-eyed Reginald Scott said to the barmaid, who just gave a knowing look and nodded.

When the old man had recovered sufficiently to talk, fortified by a few healthy mouthsful of the Guinness, he explained that a man from Walton Gaol who was serving ten years for armed robbery, had been seen three times before in the Coffee House, even though he was still alive and presumably well, in gaol. 'He always gives me a start,' said the pensioner, before taking another long sup of his Guinness.

'But that's impossible,' protested Reginald Scott, trying to rationalise what he had seen. 'How can he come here if he's banged up in prison?'

The barmaid had a theory and she began by telling Scott that he used to drink in the Coffee House. 'I think he misses his ale that much he wishes he was here, and somehow he manages to project himself here. He must love the place and have very strong willpower, that's all I can say.'

Reginald Scott was still confused by the vanishing visitor to the Coffee House, but then he recalled the uniform that the stranger had worn, and when he later described it to his brother-in-law, he was told that it was the uniform worn by the inmates of Walton Gaol.

I have investigated such 'phantasms of the living' before, and one case springs to mind because the person who was 'projecting himself' was also a prisoner in Walton Gaol. The man, Tony, had shared his cell with a well-educated civil servant named Rob, who was into Eastern mysticism and yoga. Rob first taught Tony how to meditate and then taught him how to 'astral travel', which is a way of sending the conscious mind outside of the physical body.

Tony allegedly became so proficient at astral projection, he was even able to spy on his girlfriend, and had caught her cheating on him. On one occasion, Tony even visited the Wooky Hollow club on Belmont Road and watched the singer PJ Proby perform there!

On another occasion, Tony told another inmate at the prison that his wife was seeing someone in Tranmere, and Tony was almost throttled as a result, because the other prisoner was so outraged at the assertion, claiming his wife was a loyal woman. However, a week later, this same wife wrote to her incarcerated husband to inform him that she wanted a divorce, and she eventually admitted she had been seeing a man who lived on Park Road, Tranmere.

The Ghostly Highwayman

Some very strange things have been seen in the mirrors of the Coffee House over the years. In the summer of 1984, 32-year-old Terry from Wellington Road went to the Coffee House one Wednesday evening at around 9.30pm with his girlfriend of the time, 22-year-old Cathy from Alderson Road. The couple just managed to reach the pub in time to avoid a torrential out-of-season downpour, and being midweek, they found the bar virtually empty. Terry ordered his usual pint of bitter and a half of lager for Cathy, then went to the pub toilet.

About a minute later, Cathy stormed into the gents' toilet, startling Terry, for she was in an hysterical state. Terry calmed her down and led her back into the bar.

'What's the matter, love. You gave me a bit of a shock back there. You look like you've seen a ghost or something.'

'D'you see that mirror over there behind the bar? There was a man in it ... a tall man ... I swear to god. And he was looking right at me. He wasn't any ordinary man. He was dressed in old fashioned clothes and a three cornered hat ... you know ... like the highwaymen used to wear and he had a dark cloth ... or a scarf ... and it was covering the lower half of his face. Oh, it was horrible! What do you think it was, Terry?'

'I don't know but I'm going to find out. You stay here while I go and take a look.'

Terry went to look into the mirror, but saw only his own reflection. However, about twenty minutes later, Cathy let out a stifled scream and pointed to the mirror as Terry was chatting to a friend he used to work with. Both Terry and the man clearly saw the menacing figure that Cathy had seen earlier. The man was wearing a black tricorn hat, from under which his shoulder-length hair was sprouting. A dark tartan scarf was wrapped around the lower face of the ghost, and it wore a dark green coat with wide lapels, and a light coloured frilly shirt. The apparition stood there without moving, and Terry, his friend, and Cathy did not venture any closer to it.

A regular drinker suddenly came into the pub, soaked to the skin, and as he made his entrance, the ghost in the mirror vanished instantly. Cathy was so afraid the ghost would return and possible break out of the mirror, that Terry had to ring for a taxi to take her to the Coronation Pub, several miles away.

The identity of the 'highwayman' is not known, but I hear he was last seen in the pub one evening in 2005, just before Christmas. Highwaymen were active in Wavertree and Childwall in the eighteenth century and the scarf swathed around the phantom's face to hide his features does seem to suggest that he was one of these rogues of the roads and turnpikes of bygone days.

One local historian I talked to believes the ghost in the tricorn hat may be William Clarke, hanged at Lancaster in August 1827 for highway robbery at Liverpool. Clarke is known to have had a long-term mistress in Wavertree, and in all probability, frequented the Coffee House and the Lamb Hotel.

Death Gives a Warning Through the Glass

Mirrors are the windows of the Devil, they say, and here is another supernatural tale concerning a looking glass in the Coffee House.

In 2006, 27-year-old Gina McCauley visited the Coffee House with her mother Eileen Petersen. Gina had married the year before, and after paying a visit to her mother, who lived off Wavertree's Mill Lane, she decided to go and have a drink with her before returning home to Whiston. They sat in the Coffee House upon this windy afternoon enjoying a chat, when Gina suddenly had a paranormal experience which chilled her to the marrow. She got up and went to the bar to order a bacardi for her mother and happened to look into the mirror. This was not the same mirror that the highwayman had appeared in but another mirror further down the bar.

When Gina looked at her own face in the mirror, she saw, to her horror, that her cheeks had become sunken and there were dark circles around her eyes. The cast of her face, furthermore, now had a greenish tint to it. As the young woman gazed on in horror, she saw her face disintegrate into that of a skeleton for a few seconds, before changing back.

Gina ran over to her mother and told her what she had just seen. Eileen, her mother, took her seriously and said it might have been a warning, and she advised her to perhaps go for a medical.

'Oh, Mum!' Gina exclaimed, terrified at the suggestion. 'You don't really mean I'm might die, do you?'

'Well, all I'm saying, love, is that it's better to be safe than sorry,' adding after a pause, 'Have you been feeling okay recently?'

'Mum, just shut up, will you? You're really freaking me out!' Gina told her mother, and she avoided looking at that mirror again by turning her back on it as she hurriedly gulped down her drink and left the pub clutching her mother for reassurance.

A few days later, Gina was applying her foundation when she noticed a droplet of blood on her cheek. It was coming from a large freckle. Gina telephoned her mother to tell her about it, and Eileen strongly advised her to go to the doctor's immediately, or even take a trip to the A and E at Whiston Hospital. Gina thought she was being over cautious and decided that it was probably just a pimple that had become infected. Ominously, that night, Gina's husband Toby gave his verdict, saying he thought it could be an early sign of skin cancer. Now she was worried too and first thing the next morning she went to the doctor's with Toby without even making an appointment. Toby argued with the receptionist, demanding to see the doctor, and she said they would have to wait at least an hour.

The couple sat holding hands next to each other, grim-faced, and when the doctor saw the bleeding freckle on Gina's face, he sent her straight to the local hospital, where a specialist confirmed Toby's grave suspicions – the most aggressive form of skin cancer.

Fortunately, Gina had come at the right time, because the cancerous freckle was just millimetres across, and she was successfully treated for her condition over the following six months. To this day though, Gina refuses to go anywhere near the Coffee House, where a mirror gave a warning of a possible death, but actually helped to save a life.

The Face in the Froth

One evening, in 2008, a series of strange events were reported to me at the Coffee House; events which cannot be explained.

Sixty-six-year-old drinker Don Purvis ordered a pint of 'golden' (which is made up of an equal mixture of bitter and lager) and when the drink had settled on the counter, he glanced down at the head of the beverage and noticed something quite odd; there was a face in the froth. It wasn't some random pattern made by the uneven formation of bubbles and foam; it was a distinctive face, with symmetrical eyes, a well-defined long straight nose, and a miserable, scowling, down-turned mouth. Above the top of the nose, there was a crescent shape which resembled a kiss-curl.

Don showed this face to his friend, Martin Upton, who smirked inanely and looked sceptically at Don, as if he thought he had created the face himself.

'Look, mate, I didn't do it,' Don told him with a serious look. 'I put my pint down on the bar for a second and it just appeared.'

But Martin was unconvinced and turned away and resumed a conversation he was having with a lady friend. At this point, Doug Muir, another friend of Don Purvis came into the pub and began to talk about his favourite subject, football, and Tranmere Rovers in particular. Don asked him what he was having, and Doug said he'd have a gin and bitter lemon, but then changed his mind and said he'd have a pint of Guinness instead. The barman poured the pint and placed it before Doug, who was boring Don with his blow by blow analysis of a recent Tranmere game. Don looked down at the face in his pint and saw that it had dissolved, but then he looked over at the foaming head on Doug's pint of Guinness, and there was the very same face that he had seen in the froth of his pint less than a few minutes ago.

'Hey! Seen that?' he said, interrupting his friend, who was now in full flow. He pointed to the eerie frowning face with its curled hair right above the eyes.

'Brilliant! Who did that?' Doug Muir asked, and he looked across at the young barman, expecting him to own up to having made the face.

'No, he didn't do it,' Don told him. 'I'm not having

you on. The exact same face appeared in my drink just before. Ask Mart if you don't believe me.'

'How, though? How did it get here?' Doug leaned forward, stooped, and scrutinised the face at close quarters.

'I dunno, it's really weird, isn't it?'

Don was so glad that someone else had seen the uncanny semblance of a face in their drink.

'That's happened to me!' came a loud female voice, apparently from nowhere, it made Don and Doug jump. They turned round and were confronted by a woman in her sixties with spiky peroxide-white hair and a face plastered in foundation and rouge, with two fluttering false eyelashes. It was a regular named Cindy. She was dressed in a long figure-hugging dress made of sparkling pink sequins and was tottering about on a pair of dangerously high stiletto shoes. 'On our Marie's life, on me mother's death bed,' she said, making a miniature sign of the cross on her ample chest, 'that same face you see there just appeared in my drink. I'm anaemic, you see, and the doctor himself told me to have a regular glass of Guinness because of the iron in it, and when was it? Yes, it must have been the week before Good Friday, I was just going to have a sip, and our Marie, she's me youngest, she saw it first. She said, "Mam, look at that!" and I said, "Look at what?" and she pointed to the face. I went cold. I didn't drink it; are you going to drink that?'

'Er, yeah, s'pose so, I'm not really superstitious,' Doug said, backing away. He was more afraid of Cindy than any paranormal forces that may be doodling faces in the top of his pint. He excused himself and headed for a secluded corner table and he beckoned Don to follow him.

'Your mate's nice, isn't he?' said Cindy, blocking Don's way.

He nodded nervously with a bright false smile, then quickly darted away to join his friend in the corner. Then Cindy sauntered off unsteadily to another part of the pub, much to the relief of Don and Doug. The two chatted together about politics, football (Doug made sure of that) and recent telly programmes. Doug got the next round in and when he came back, he and Don sat and watched a face form in the frothy head of each pint. Doug quickly shouted to his much younger friend Martin Upton.

'Marty, come over here, mate and have a look at this quick!'

Martin reluctantly left his female friend, saying, 'I won't be a tic. I'd better go and see what this pair of jokers want, don't go away,' and he dashed over to the table and saw for himself the faces in the froth.

'I hope this isn't some kind of stupid joke, Doug. Can't you see I'm talking to this lovely girl over there.' He examined the faces in the drinks and noticed they were identical. 'It's odd, like,' Martin conceded. 'I'll give you that.' But he had more important matters to attend to and he went back to rejoin his beautiful female acquaintance.

The bar and parlour of the Coffee House steadily filled as the night progressed and the faces in the drinks episode was eventually forgotten but, at around 10.40pm, Don Purvis returned to his table in the corner with a glass of scotch and lemonade for Doug, and as he sat down, he saw another face appearing in the pint of lager he had also just ordered. It looked very similar to the other faces that had materialised, only this one was smiling.

'Someone's not at rest,' Doug Muir said, rather enigmatically, upon seeing the latest face forming in the froth.

'What d'you mean?' Don asked him.

'I don't know,' said Doug, 'I just have a feeling someone, or something, unearthly is in here tonight. Maybe the spirit of someone who's died and can't rest. That's all I'm saying.'

And then Don Purvis saw him.

He looked up, and there, standing stock-still around the corner of the bar counter, was a man – tall, painfully thin, with a long pale face, small button eyes, a long straight nose, grinning mouth and that c-shaped kiss curl across his forehead. His face and hair looked exactly like the features Don and Doug had seen in the heads of their drinks. The face of the stranger was so unusually pallid, it seemed almost clown-like.

Don tapped his friend's forearm and out of the side of his mouth, in a low voice, whispered: 'Hey! Seen him over there?'

'Who?' Doug asked. Then he noticed the stranger, who was wearing a white shirt and black tie under a black jacket. He shuddered and felt his heart shrink, because he instantly recognised the face as well.

'Don't stare, he looks unbalanced,' said Don, and he deliberately looked down at the table, then up at the ceiling, but his left eye swivelled involuntarily and he winced. The weird man in black was still staring over at them.

'Flippin' 'eck, he looks weird,' said Doug under his breath, 'I've never seen him in here before. What's his problem? What's he looking at us for?'

Don stood up and reached over to Martin Upton, who was now staring intently at his phone, composing a text message intended for the girl he'd chatted to earlier. 'What?' Martin said, slightly irritated, as the latter tapped his arm. As inconspicuously as possible, Don drew Martin's attention to the grinning man in black standing at the bar, and Martin said, 'Oh my god! His face looks like the face we saw in your ale.'

Despite this, his attention was quickly drawn back to the composition of the text message.

'Don't you think it's odd. Have you ever seen him in here before?' Don asked.

'No,' answered Martin, without taking his eyes off the mobile screen.

'Hey, Don! He's gone!' Doug suddenly said, and Don and Martin looked back to the spot where they had seen the man in black just a second before to find that he had vanished.

Closing time soon came and Don Purvis and Doug Muir left the Coffee House and parted on Fir Lane. Doug went to his house on Bristol Road, and Don carried on down Fir Lane, a lonely place after dark and a spooky one too, because it runs alongside the cemetery of Holy Trinity church. All the way down that lane, Don couldn't drive that weird face in the ale froth from his mind or the face of that man in black who had stared at him with those penetrating beady eyes, though the two were barely distinguishable. Then he heard footsteps following him down the dimly lit lane, and so he stopped … and so did the footfalls. He must have only heard the echo of his own footsteps. He smiled, exhaled with relief, and walked along Prince Alfred Road on this moonless night eager to be safely home.

Minutes later, Don had turned down Grant Avenue and was soon putting his key into the front door of his new home, an upstairs flat in a terraced house on Winchfield Road. He had lived there for just over a week and liked the proximity of the flat to the park across the road (nicknamed The Mystery).

41

Don was a confirmed bachelor and now he had retired from his white-collar job in the council, his only way of passing the time was pottering about on his allotment, an occasional flutter on the horses, the telly and the pub. On this evening, he was glad to get to bed since he had risen earlier than normal, but a good night's sleep was not to be his. No sooner had he stripped down to his underwear, than he heard footsteps outside in the street. He looked out of the window and his heart somersaulted. A man in a black suit was standing on the pavement below, staring up at Don's bedroom window – and it was that same man, the weird stranger from the pub.

Don backed away from the window but he knew all too well that the man had seen him looking out. What should he do? Call the police? But what would he say to them if he did call them? The stranger hadn't committed any crime ... yet.

Suddenly he became aware of footsteps in the hallway. Had the man in black now entered the house? A quick look out of the window confirmed that the stranger had left his position on the pavement. Before he could come up with a plan of action he heard someone come up the stairs with superhuman speed! Dunk-dunk-dunk-dunk-dunk ... he was already at the door ... and the door-handle was starting to turn. Don rushed across the room and seized the handle with both hands to try and stop it turning, but it was no use. The person on the other side of that door had terrific strength, so Don threw his right shoulder against the door, but it relentlessly inched open until four long white slender fingers tipped with dark and dirty nails came into view sliding around the edge of the door. At the same time Don heard chilling laughter coming from behind that door and the pensioner screamed for help at the top of his voice. Moments later, he heard sounds down in the hall. Someone was coming to help him.

The hall light went on, and its reassuring beam shone into the bedroom. In that second the ox of a man behind the door vanished and now, with nothing to resist Don's effort, the bedroom door slammed shut. It soon became apparent that the sounds in the hall had come from the two elderly sisters who lived downstairs coming up to complain about the noise. Rather than admitting that he had just had a battle of strength with a ghost, Don muttered something about having experienced a particularly lucid nightmare and apologised to the women; there was nothing amiss and they should go back to bed, it was very late.

As soon as the two old spinsters had tottered back down the stairs, Don switched on his television turning the volume down very low so as not to disturb them again. The sound of human voices coming from the box cheered him; it was his substitute for real company. He wondered if he should go and stay in Doug's house on Bristol Road but decided against it because he knew Doug's wife wasn't keen on him even in daylight hours, never mind at this ungodly hour of the morning. Don turned all the lights on in his flat, and carefully drew the curtains so that no one could see in. He then had time to ponder on what had happened just a matter of minutes ago. Was he losing his mind? Was this the first sign of that disease which he dreaded most at this time of his life – Alzheimer's?

No, that was nonsense, something truly supernatural had taken place; he had definitely been visited by a ghost, but why? And what had been the significance of the faces in the froths of the drinks, and was there really a connection? Don went to bed but sat up, propped against four pillows. He watched the dire programmes on the cable channels until he finally dozed off and when he awoke, startled by some noise in the street, he saw to his relief that morning was now here and he relished the welcoming din of the milkman placing bottles on doorsteps.

Around noon, Don telephoned Doug and asked to meet him at the Wellington pub, which is situated at the junction of the Picton, Rathbone, and Wellington roads. Doug suggested they meet at the Coffee House but Don said he felt very wary of that pub since the supernatural events of the night before and insisted on a rendezvous at the Welly (as the Wellington pub is nicknamed by some locals).

At ten past one Doug walked into the pub as arranged, and Don immediately bought him a drink. At this time there were only six or seven drinkers in the place and Don and Doug sat in a quiet corner in the parlour where Don hoped no one could overhear their conversation. In whispered tones Don told Doug about the ghostly visit and Doug knew he was telling the truth from the look of fear on his face as he relived the bizarre incident.

'Why is it haunting me?' Don asked, racking his brains. 'I can't get it out of my mind.'

'Maybe you should get the house blessed,' was Doug's advice and he suggested Don visit the vicar of Holy Trinity Church.

Despite Don's efforts at privacy, an old man in his eighties named Barney had edged closer to them while they were talking in order to come into earshot. Picking up his pint up from his table, he walked over to Don and Doug and stood there for a moment, as if he was figuring out how to frame what he wanted to say. Finally he came out with it: 'Are you the two blokes who saw faces in their drinks at the Coffee House last night?'

News travels fast round here, Don thought, and nodded, eyeing the man suspiciously. 'Yeah, who told you about that?'

'Can I just join you a moment, and then I'll be off,' said Barney.

'Yes, go on then,' said Doug, and he moved his stool away from the table slightly, scraping its legs against the carpet.

Once seated Barney leaned in close to the two men, 'A man hanged himself in the Coffee House, a long time ago, in the 1920s. He was a barman there and his name was Wright. He was infatuated with the landlord's daughter but she didn't want to know, and one night after the pub had just closed, he hanged himself. He left a note to the landlord's daughter, but she never received it. Her father chucked it in the fire. Suppose he didn't want her upset or anything. Not long after that, the staff and drinkers at the Coffee House started to see Wright's face in the froth of their drinks. My father witnessed this at first hand, and he was a very religious man ... never lied.'

'What did this fella Wright look like?' Doug asked. 'Can you remember?'

Barney smirked, 'I'm not that old, lad, I just look it. I wasn't born till 1926.'

'Oh, sorry, mate' said Doug. 'Can I get you a drink?'

Barney shook his head. 'Nah, it's alright, lad, I've got to get off soon. I've got to go to the clinic.'

'I wonder where this Mr Wright lived?' Don said, wondering if Barney had any idea.

'Matter of fact I do know,' said Barney. 'He lived right over there,' and he pointed to the parlour wall, 'just there across the park.'

45

Don's heart skipped a beat. Barney coughed and then gave a thoughtful pause. 'Winchfield Road, facing my uncle's.'

That was enough. There and then, Don decided he was leaving his new home, and within a week, he had found new accommodation in a flat overlooking Sefton Park.

THE POSTE HOUSE
Cumberland Street, off Dale Street

Ghosts of the Poste House

Hidden away from the thoroughfares of the city centre since the early nineteenth century, the Poste House is a gem of a pub at 23 Cumberland Street, a quiet little lane which runs between Dale Street and Victoria Street.

In the so-called *'Diary of Jack the Ripper'*, which I and many other Ripperologists believed to be a poorly-constructed fake journal, there is a line, supposedly written by the Ripper himself, in which he states that he 'took refreshment at the Poste House'. In 1888, the year the diary is supposed to have been written, the Poste House was actually called the New Post Office Hotel, and did not receive its new name, Poste House, until the 1980s, so how could Jack the Ripper have predicted what the pub was going to be called almost a century after his death? If the *Diary of Jack the Ripper* was forged, and I believe it was, the forger did not do his homework, and the Poste House clanger is just one of the many glaring mistakes which he made.

Jack the Ripper may not have supped ale at the Poste House but a man of much greater notoriety is also said to have visited the establishment: Adolf Hitler. For many years, the rumour has persisted that the Austrian dictator came to Liverpool in his early twenties and stayed with his half-brother Alois Hitler at Upper Stanhope Street in 1912. Alois Hitler did live on Upper Stanhope Street with his Irish wife Bridget, and that is a fact that can be verified in the 1911 census, but whether Adolf stayed with them is more difficult to prove. In my youth, my mother told me that Hitler had lived 'down in the south-end' just before the First World War and she told me how my grandmother had known this from her friend – a woman with a strong Northern Irish accent named Maggie Prentice, who supposedly had the psychic gift of second sight.

Maggie, a laundress, also read tea leaves and could interpret playing cards (cartomancy) to foretell the future. She had read the palm of a young Hitler and warned him that he would be given a great power by a higher force but he should be careful how he used it or he'd end up causing many deaths and would ultimately end his own.

I went looking for such a Mrs Prentice and discovered her in several censuses. She was born in Belfast and had lived in Toxteth during Hitler's alleged stay in Liverpool. Bridget Hitler backed this strange claim in her unfinished *Memoirs of Bridget Hitler*, which was discovered in the New York Library in the 1970s and she too mentions a Mrs Prentice.

It may all be hot air and coincidences, or maybe a young Hitler really did drift about as a penniless down-and-out in Liverpool in 1912. Why, if he had decided to make a new life for himself in America, he might even have boarded the *Titanic*. The history of the world and the path of our civilisation would have taken fundamental turn if Hitler had drowned in the North Atlantic ocean.

Whilst there is no record of Jack the Ripper or Adolf Hitler's visits to the Poste House, there is a factual record of one prominent historical personage gracing the backstreet drinking establishment and that person was no less than Prince Charles Louis Napoleon Bonaparte (1808-1873) who, after his escape from the fortress of Ham in May 1846, sought exile in England and came to Liverpool at one point, and drank at the New Post Office Hotel on Cumberland Street.

He subsequently returned to France, later marrying a Spanish countess and becoming the Emperor for a decade after being elected by seven million votes. He ended his days in exile at Kent. Other, less famous, but much more colourful characters have frequented the Poste House. A swindler from Nantymoel in South Wales named Davy Roberts, for example, was a regular at the pub, and would extract money and drinks from the gullible by informing them in a perfect southern Irish accent that he was the uncrowned King of Ireland, a direct descendant of King Cormac Longbeard, who had been robbed of his right to the throne by 'that bastard

Cromwell' during the English Civil War.

Roberts would produce official-looking deeds proclaiming the impending recovery of his vast estates, and the silver-tongued Welsh confidence trickster promised many a fleeced drinker that they would become princes and barons at his Royal court when he returned to the throne of Erin. They say Davy Roberts dropped dead in the toilets of the Poste House one evening, probably from the effects of alcohol poisoning.

Another despicable regular at the Poste House in Victorian times was Jack Garratt, a Tranmere alcoholic who once sold his teenaged wife (who was mute) to a sea captain for ten guineas and who also once convinced the staff at the pub that the landlord had just enjoyed a huge win on the horses and wanted everyone to have a drink on the house.

At the time, the landlord, George Barratt, was paying a cordial visit to his friend, Joseph Emsley Wright, an auctioneer, at the latter's premises on Dale Street, just around the corner from the Poste House. When the landlord Barratt heard about his supposed win on the horses and his alleged instructions for drinks on the house, he instantly barred Garratt from his premises for good, and tried, unsuccessfully, to prosecute him.

The Poste House has been haunted by several ghosts over the years, and the year 1895 stands out in its supernatural history because of two startling hauntings, both witnessed at close quarters by the landlord of the time, the aforementioned George Barratt.

On the afternoon of Wednesday, 22 May 1895, Nance Kelly, a woman who claimed to be of Romany descent, visited the New Post Office Hotel and read the palms of several drinkers there. One of them was Henry Shaw, an odd-job man who lived at 8 Gerard Street, off Scotland Road. Shaw was a friend of the pub landlord, and became concerned when old Nance looked at his palm and immediately adopted a stern expression and then warned him against working with ladders.

Just a week ago, Shaw had cleaned the windows of the pub on his ladder, which was one of the important items of his livelihood. George Barratt ordered Nance to get out of the pub and as she left, she also predicted that Barratt would suffer from gout, and that it would be the precursor of a forthcoming tragedy. Having delivered her stark predictions, the gypsy left the room full of silent drinkers without a backward glance.

Sure enough, that evening, Barratt experienced a sharp pain in his big toe, and upon removing his shoe and sock, he noticed that one side of his toe had a reddish swelling to it, one of the early indications of gout. The painful lump enlarged over the next few days and the gout lasted for almost three weeks.

Then, on the Wednesday afternoon of 12 June of that year, Henry Shaw was told by George Barratt to give a touch of paint to the sign over the pub doorway. Accordingly, Shaw propped his ladder against the wall, and climbed it to a height of a mere 14 feet. Moments later, probably by some careless misplacing of his foot, Henry Shaw fell and literally cracked his head open on the pavement.

He looked up questioningly at George Barratt and several drinkers in wide-eyed shock, and as he uttered something about his wife, blood began to spurt from the fallen man's nose and ears. He quickly lost consciousness as several people ran off in search of a doctor. Henry Shaw was then conveyed to the Northern

Hospital, but died of his head injuries on the following day.

Several of the drinkers at the Cumberland Street pub recalled the chilling warning given by the gypsy Nance Kelly when she read Shaw's palm, advising him to be very careful when working with ladders. Barratt dismissed this talk with a shrug, arguing that it was just a coincidence, and that anyone with half a brain knew that Henry Shaw, being a handyman and the pub window cleaner, would obviously work with ladders, but this explanation didn't wash with the superstitious drinkers, for they wondered how Nance Kelly had also been able to predict the gout which would afflict the landlord in the run up to the fatal accident.

Then Henry Shaw returned, a week after his physical body had been lowered into the mouth of a grave in Anfield Cemetery. At the time of the first ghostly visitation, George Barratt had collected a small sum of money from various business acquaintances for the widowed Mrs Shaw and when the landlord had presented the money to the widow at her home on Gerard Street, she had told him that Harry, as she had called her late husband, had visited her during the night with his head bandaged, telling her he wanted her to join him, as he loved her so much.

She had told the ghost to go back to the place allotted to him by the Lord, but Harry wouldn't hear of it and said he wanted to come back into the world of the living.

'Mr Barratt,' the widow Shaw chillingly added, and he felt his blood go cold, 'Harry misses you and his work so much. He's clinging on to us, you see, Mr Barratt, and as God is my judge, I know he's listening to me right now, and I feel as if he's going to try and come back.'

George Barratt advised Mrs Shaw to see a priest, and hurriedly left the old dwelling. Dusk hadn't yet fallen but the landlord was convinced that he could hear footsteps close behind him all the way from Gerard Street to Cumberland Street. Barratt slept uneasily that night and suffered a recurring nightmare about Shaw's fall from the ladder and the spraying of his blood from his nostrils and ears.

Three days passed, after which came the strange news which filtered its way into the landlord's ears by way of overheard gossip. A plumber named Jim Kennedy told a tailor named John Butter that a man with a heavily-bandaged head had been spotted looking through the windows of the pub the previous afternoon. A Mrs Castle and two other curious drinkers had rushed outside to see who he was, only to find the street empty.

The landlord confronted Mrs Castle when she came into the pub, and asked her about the bandaged head, and she confirmed the plumber's story. Then another drinker, a coalman named Hughes, claimed he had actually seen the man with the bandaged head earlier that morning before the pub was even open. He had been pacing up and down past the pub's front door before suddenly vanishing. The coalman looked at Barratt with a sheepish expression, as if he was holding something back, then came out with it. 'I swear it looked for all the world like the late Henry Shaw,' he said.

George Barratt knew Hughes was a simple down-to-earth coalman, who was not known for such fanciful imaginings, so the drinker's words made him very uneasy. He tried to change the subject but the ever-popular subject of ghosts cannot be so easily brushed aside. One of the drinkers who was sitting in the corner of the pub put forward the theory that the spirit of the deceased odd-job man was not at rest because of the untimely and violent manner of his death, and many of the other drinkers nodded their agreement. As more punters came into the pub, the talk of the ghost became the ruling topic of conversation.

At 10.30pm, the drinkers were still talking in hushed voices about the bandaged head peering through the window and the pacing spectre outside the pub door, when a loud clattering sound was heard. All conversation stopped dead. Something was knocking against the downstairs window of the pub. George Barratt rested his pipe on the bar and lifted the hinged section of the counter to investigate the noise. Every eye in the pub was on the curtains as Barratt slowly slid them back to reveal the top of a ladder, silhouetted against the glare of the lamp-post outside. It was Henry Shaw's ladder. A woman's scream ripped through the smoky atmosphere of the bar, making everyone jump, and then came the faint sound of a chuckle outside. It turned out to be black-humoured pranksters messing about outside and by the time Barratt had opened the pub door, they had disappeared off into the night.

Then, at three that morning, when Barratt and his wife were sound asleep in their bed, they were both roused from their well-earned slumbers by a shout. 'George!'

The familiar voice echoed in the street outside, and because the previous day had been one of record sunshine, the Irish Sea had thrown a resulting fog over the port. Barratt went to the window, parted the curtains, and looked out into the swirling eddies of vapour, and could just make out a silhouette with a light-coloured head. He lifted open the window but his wife screamed, 'Don't! You'll let the fog in; come back to bed, it's just a drunk.'

But it wasn't a drunk, as George could now plainly see. It was Henry Shaw, standing forlornly in the fog on the pavement below, with his bandaged head. His face and hands were almost as white as the bandage that swathed his cracked head.

'George! I've come back,' shouted the ghost, 'but the wife won't have me near her.'

George Barratt staggered backwards from the window, and his heart pounded so hard, the carotid blood rush made his neck move and his head shook. 'No,' was all he could muster.

'Ooh! Close that window, George!' said Mrs Barratt drawing herself into a foetal position, as she too had heard the ghost's words.

'Let me in, George,' said Henry Shaw's phantom, 'and I'll do any work that needs doing.'

George Barratt swore, something he would normally never do in front of his wife but this was an exceptional situation. 'You're dead now, Henry!' he shouted, 'Go away!' and he slammed the window down with such force that the impact cracked one of the panes. George fastened the catch on the window and raced back to bed, where he and his wife clung to one another under the blankets as they listened to the troubled ghost still shouting in the street.

'Our Father, who art in Heaven ...' Mrs Barratt started to recite with her eyes squeezed shut, and her husband quickly joined in. It had been many a year since he had last said the Lord's Prayer, but he still recalled every word.

Tap! Tap! Tap! Henry was knocking at the bedroom window, and Mrs Barratt peeped over the edge of the blanket, then screamed and plunged back under the covers. George Barratt exclaimed, 'Sweet Jesus!' as he beheld the terrifying sight at the window. He should have closed the curtains back over, for there was Henry with his bandaged head and his flour-white face, gazing in through the cracked window pane with black skull-socket eyes. His index fingernail tapped on the window, and then his hands reached for the bottom of the window and tried to lift it.

'Our Father! Who art in Heaven!' bawled the pub landlord louder and louder, until at last he saw the apparition of his former friend float away from the window and vanish into the fog.

George Barratt and his wife held their breath. Had he really gone? Then, when he was finally convinced the ghost had gone, he started to reassure his wife as he rocked her gently in his arms. 'It's gone now, my love,' he said over and over again. 'Don't worry, it's gone.'

Not until the pale dawn light had permeated the fog did the couple manage to grab some sleep. Bibles and crucifixes were placed around the Barratt's bedroom on the following day, and a few of the drinkers heard from Mrs Donovan, a cleaner at the local church, how the landlord had procured the holy books and crucifixes from the priest, and this naturally set tongues wagging.

Then an eccentric old man, known only as Mr Tavistock, called at the pub on Cumberland Street, and asked Mrs Barratt if her husband was about. Tavistock claimed he was an exorcist and a professional 'ghost layer'. He mentioned several local hauntings he had successfully dealt with, and many of the drinkers present confirmed both the hauntings and his dealings with them. Tavistock unequivically assured the landlord's wife that he could rid the pub of Shaw's ghost, and during the conversation, George Barratt came into the pub. He took Tavistock upstairs to try and ascertain whether or not he was a crackpot or a genuine exorcist. Barratt listened to the old man, who had the air of a cleric about him, and quickly realised that he seemed to know what he was talking about. Tavistock talked of the mind's survival of 'bodily death', of the willpower of spirits and their techniques of manifestation, and he showed the landlord several scars he had received from objects hurled at him by poltergeists and the like during his unusual career.

Cutting to the chase, Barratt asked, 'How much do you require for this task, Mr Tavistock?'

'Twenty-five guineas, and you'll never hear from Shaw again,' the old man replied.

The requested sum was paid to Tavistock there and then, and minutes later, the old man asked the landlord where Henry Shaw was buried. Barratt told him exactly where the unmarked grave was in Anfield Cemetery, two gravestones to the left of a relative of his own, in fact. Next, the silver-haired occultist asked to be shown the precise spot where Shaw had fallen from the ladder. Barratt took him outside, and when two of the drinkers followed, the landlord told them to go back indoors. They did so, but their insatiable curiosity brought them straight to the windows.

'Here,' said Barratt, indicating the spot on the pavement where Shaw's skull had been cracked to reveal his brains. 'This is where he hit his head.'

'Was there blood here?' Tavistock asked, kneeling on

the cold ground and examining the pavement with his bespectacled eyes.

'Yes, plenty,' Barratt sighed, intrigued.

Tavistock then mumbled something unintelligible and produced a small clasp knife from his coat pocket, and an envelope from his inside coat pocket. He scraped the blade of the knife between the cracks, and unearthed a quantity of dirt, which he used to smear over the interior of the envelope. Those smears were brownish red. 'I need his blood, you see, when it's possible ...' Tavistock's words trailed away, swallowed up by his incomprehensible mumbo-jumbo. He was then helped to his feet by the landlord and without a word of explanation he walked off.

'Is that it?' Barratt shouted after him.

Without even turning to say goodbye out of common courtesy, Tavistock said, 'No, I shall be back later.'

George Barratt wondered if that would be the last he'd see of the co-called ghost-layer, and when he told his wife what had happened, she shook her head and said, 'A fool and his money are soon parted.'

But Tavistock, true to his word, returned to the New Post Office Hotel that night at 9pm. Carrying a portmanteau, he came through the door as the pub was crowded with drinkers, and he went straight up to the counter wearing an exhausted look on his face. He told Barratt something he couldn't comprehend. 'He's in Purgatory, your friend, and he's a very stubborn spirit.'

The landlord asked his wife to take his place behind the counter and took the old mystic upstairs, and in the quiet of the living room, Tavistock sat and rummaged through his portmanteau. Eventually he located what he was looking for and produced a crude cross, bound together with a red thread. 'This is a rowan cross, it repels spirits, especially evil ones. Mr Shaw's spirit is one of the worst kind though, because it isn't evil, just pesky.'

'So what am I supposed do with this cross?' Barratt asked.

'Hang it on the wall in your bedroom, and he won't come near it. But I may burn this afterwards if he still won't stay away,' and Tavistock took a strange effigy of a little man out of the case. 'Made from the very clay of Shaw's grave, mixed with his blood.'

Barratt recoiled with shock. 'You've been digging at his grave?'

Tavistock shot him a brief smile to allay the landlord's consternation. 'Do not be alarmed, Mr Barratt, I know what I am doing. I have baptised this effigy with holy water and given it the same name as the deceased. If I burn it, all earthly ties between Shaw's ghost and this world will be severed for good, believe me.'

'So when are you going to burn it? And where are you going to burn it?'

'If it's convenient, I should burn it at one in the morning, when the forces of the occult world enter fully into our world. I should burn it on these premises to maximise the effect.' Tavistock explained, then coughed and with a shiver said, 'I am chilled to the bone from my work at the cemetery; may I have a whiskey sir?'

'Of course,' Barratt replied, and fetched a whisky from downstairs. By half-past midnight, the last drinker had left the pub, and the door was locked. At five minutes to one that morning, a fog had lain its ashen shroud from the Mersey, across the lamp-lit streets of Liverpool to the dark suburbs, and upon this eerie night,

George Barratt and his wife still sat downstairs in the pub. Tavistock sat with them, on a stool before a fire that had been kindled especially for the ghost-banishing ritual. He held the baptised, blood-impregnated effigy of Henry Shaw in his bony fingers, ready to commit it to the flames at the appointed time.

'What was that?' Mrs Barratt's face suddenly turned to face the windows. 'Listen!' she said, then looked down at the floor, straining her ears.

'What?' George Barratt asked, as he too made an effort to listen. 'It's just a dog barking somewhere in the distance,' he decided.

Mrs Barratt shook her head ever so slowly. 'No, George, it was him. He shouted you.'

'Fear has magnifying eyes, and makes devil's footsteps from a dripping tap,' said Tavistock.

George ...' came an agonised voice from outside, making Mrs Barratt react with a jolt.

'It's him!' the landlord whispered to Tavistock, who simply smiled at the strange proceedings in a reassuringly calm manner.

The old man eyed the clock on the wall. 'Just three minutes to go,' he said, 'let him speak his last.'

'George, please just let me fix a slate, or point the wall in your yard!' cried the pathetic ghost.

'Be gone, spirit!' shouted the landlord.

'But, George! Please let me in!' the ghost cried in a mournful voice, then began shaking the door of the pub.

'Henry Shaw,' intoned Tavistock, with the assertiveness of a self-righteous preacher in the pulpit, 'I release you from this Purgatory! I cut all the earthly bonds of love and hate, of animosity and kinship ...'

'No!' screamed the ghost beyond the front door.

'Cease that!' said a voice in the corner of the room. It came from a man in a three-pointed hat, dressed in clothes from the days of Boswell and Dr Johnson. Tavistock, for all of his alleged years of ghost-laying and his many confrontations with the unknown, seemed very startled at the appearance of this ghost. The Barratts, meanwhile, had retreated into the corner diagonally opposite the corner where the apparition had manifested itself.

'Who are you, spirit?' Tavistock asked, as he reached into the pocket of his waistcoat for a silver crucifix.

'There is no need for you to use that,' said the man in the tricorn hat, stepping out of the shadows. He had rosy cheeks and a rather plump and friendly face. 'I am what you may understand to be a spirit guide, and I have come to take Henry Shaw to the appointed place.'

Tavistock 'tested' the ghost to see if it was in league with the Devil. 'Do you believe that Jesus Christ was the Son of God, spirit?'

'Yes, I do, Mr Tavistock, but you must cease your amateur messing in the world of spirit for monetary gain,' the guide told him, walking to the door of the pub, 'no good can come of such commercial gain.'

The Barratts watched in horror as the guide unbolted the door and admitted the emotionally-torn ghost of Henry Shaw. His snow-white face was glistening with tears, and he squinted at the lamps of the well-lit parlour. He slowly came up the single step into the pub, and smiled, but the smile didn't extend to his eyes, which remained achingly sad.

'Henry Shaw,' said the eighteenth century-attired guide, 'I am here to take you to the place put aside for your soul. You may bid goodbye to your friend.'

61

'Goodbye George ... Mrs Barratt,' said Henry, and the guide took his hand, led him outside into the fog, and before Tavistock and the Barratts could reach the doorway, they saw a flash of golden light which lit up fogbound Cumberland Street.

The landlord, his wife and the old exorcist could detect the sweet scent of violets after they had gone. After that eventful morning, the tormented ghost of Henry Shaw was seen no more, but Tavistock told George Barratt that he felt there was something beneath the very foundations of his public house, perhaps an ancient well, or a forgotten megalithic standing stone, because the old man was sensitive to a subtle energy he called telluric lines of force. This mysterious energy was streaming from the earth far beneath the building, from something just above the sandstone bedrock, Tavistock claimed, and he said that, in his experience, such places where this power was active became a magnet for ghosts and other supernatural phenomena.

'And how many guineas do you require to fix this new problem?' asked the landlord sarcastically. The reply worried George Barratt, because it was obviously a genuine one.

'All the wealth of the world could not stop that force, sir,' said Tavistock, 'I am merely drawing your attention to the force and warning you of it. The only way to avoid this force would be for you to move this public house brick by brick to another location, or for you to move to another pub.'

The telluric force described by Tavistock is a very real but poorly understood energy usually associated with dowsers, and dowsing is connected, of course, with underground water. Man creates his laws and by-laws, but Nature is the only true law, and her ways are cloaked in mystery.

Beneath the streets of Liverpool, there are many wells and springs. Just one of the these wells can be seen at Number 80, Bold Street, of all places. The well came to light when the shop was being renovated, and the shop owner had the walls of the well reinforced and extended. The source of the water which feeds the wells and springs of Liverpool remain a mystery, as does the origin of the seas of Earth as a whole. Geologists believe that the creation of water takes place deep within the earth's interior, but the chemistry involved still remains a mystery. The late naturalist Loren Eisley once wrote of water: 'Its substance reaches everywhere; it touches the past and prepares the future; it moves under the poles and wanders thinly in the heights of the air. If there is magic on this planet, it is contained in water.'

The Celts, whose genes are carried by a large percentage of Liverpool's population, believed the Earth to be the Great Mother, the supporter and sustainer of all life, who nourished the world by a network of invisible arteries, which carried a life force to all living things. The channels and power were known as Woivre, which means snake-like, and was sometimes manifested in underground streams of the type which flow under Liverpool.

There are undoubtedly places on the surface of the earth which have more than their fair share of paranormal activity in the form of ghosts, UFOs and so on, and such a nexus of earth energy may exist under the Poste House. This theory concerning earth energy may be born out by the following report.

In December 1882, before George Barratt had moved

in as landlord of the New Post Office Hotel, the pub on Cumberland Street was the scene of a very unusual incident. Jane Crossing, a 29-year-old barmaid, and several startled drinkers, witnessed the sudden materialisation of a six-foot-tall 'hissing blue flame' that erupted from the floor behind the counter of the pub. This flame gave off no heat, merely a royal blue phosphorescence, and some of those who saw it undulate before them claimed to see strange faces in the manifestation. After a few seconds, the flame shrank into the floor and vanished as mysteriously as it had appeared. Being a native of Devon, Jane the barmaid later said she had seen similar ghostly 'flames' appear in the remote wilds of Dartmoor, but they were explained away as being mere will-o'-the-wisp, or leakages of built-up methane gas from beneath the soil.

About four months after the 1895 haunting of the New Post Office Hotel by the ghost of Henry Shaw, there was another ghostly visitation at the pub, and on this occasion, not one but two apparitions were seen.

On the night of 31 October, Halloween, the landlord of the pub on Cumberland Street was eagerly awaiting the arrival of two close friends, known as Mickey and Johnno, who were due to pay a visit from Manchester. Both lads were in their twenties, and both were accomplished musicians who could play the piano, banjo, harmonica and the penny whistle. Whenever they visited Liverpool, they always called in at George Barratt's pub and would sit side by side as they played the upright piano in the pub's parlour.

When Mickey and Johnno failed to turn up, George Barratt assumed they had either been delayed by something or other, or perhaps they had a business

64

commitment. The Barratts retired to bed that Halloween night, but at around one o'clock in the morning, the couple were awakened by the sounds of a piano playing somewhere close by. Then they realised with horror that the slow, peculiar-sounding melody was coming from the piano in their own pub, so Mr Barratt assumed a lunatic had broken into the pub, for a burglar of any sense would not alert anyone to his presence by playing a piano in the dead of night.

The landlord took his old pistol from the dresser drawer, and, against his wife's wishes, crept downstairs with a lighted candle. Opening the door leading to the parlour, George Barratt saw something that would give him nightmares until the day he died. Two skeleton were sitting side by side on the seat in front of the piano, playing Chopin's Funeral March.

You can't kill a dead man, but the beleaguered landlord, out of sheer heart-stopping terror, fired his pistol once at the skeleton nearest to him, then turned and ran upstairs, dropping the candle in the retreat. He then barricaded himself and his wife in the bedroom until dawn.

The following day, George Barratt received the tragic news that Mickey and Johnno were dead. Mickey had died of a typhoid-like fever a week or so ago, shortly followed by his friend Johnno, who had drunk so much to drown his sorrows at losing his best mate that he had fallen down some stairs after losing his footing and broken his neck.

The landlord pictured the two skeletons he had seen at the piano the night before, playing a song that was synonymous with death.

Believe it or not, we have not yet finished with the

ghosts of the Poste House. In early Edwardian times, the New Post Office Hotel came into the hands of Gertrude Macqueen, and during her tenure in 1902, there were reports of glasses and bottles being thrown at customers by an invisible hand and an intriguing account of the pub clock going backwards from 9pm. A clock-mender was called out to investigate but could find nothing wrong with the mechanism, which afterwards returned to normal.

In 1904, a woman in black, wearing a dark veil, came into the pub, and silently walked around, stopping in front of each startled drinker to study his face, before moving on to the next one. She then left the pub and vanished into thin air on Cumberland Street. Could she be the same spectre mentioned in the following report?

In the late 1970s, a hansom cab, looking as if it had come straight out of the Victorian or Edwardian era, is said to have pulled up at the pub one evening at 10.20pm, and a man in a top hat and opera cloak alighted from the quaint-looking vehicle, linking arms with a woman dressed in black funereal clothes, including a black 'coal-box' bonnet and a mantilla veil.

The caped man helped her down from the hansom cab, paid the cabby who sat atop the antiquated vehicle, before walking into the Poste House with his female companion. People in the pub who had witnessed the arrival of the hansom cab through the windows waited for the couple to come inside. The door of the pub duly opened, and footsteps were heard to enter the premises, but the people who made them could not be seen. Seconds afterwards, the hansom cab trundled away and the clip-clop of the horse pulling the cab faded away. Several drinkers who went outside were baffled to

66

witness that the hansom and its horse disappeared into thin air before turning the corner in the road.

I receive emails and letters every now and then from people who have experienced strange cold spots and the sensation of being touched on their leg or arm when they are in the Poste House, so it would seem that the old pub is still being frequented by spirits of the non-alcoholic kind.

THE SWAN INN
Wood Street

In a backstreet, far removed from the roar of everyday
life, you will find the louder roar of a very different kind
of life within the walls of the legendary Swan Inn, a pub
that is like no other, and a pub that has resisted the type
of insidious corporate gentrification and 'ponsification'
that has turned other grass-roots drinking establishments
into indistinguishable neon and chrome clones. Behind
the blue tiles and stained glass of the Swan Inn's facade,
you're likely to rub shoulders with people from every
culture and subculture, and from all walks of life, ranging
from rockers, Goths and Wiccans, to bank managers,
bikers, worn-out white-collar workers and students; all
human life is there and the spectrum of regulars is as

varied as the Swan's range of beers.

The history of the Swan Inn is just as colourful as the regulars who frequent it, and what follows is but a small collection of strange incidents that have taken place within one of the last of the independent traditional British pubs.

Witches Stay Away from My Door!

The pub sign of the Swan may state that it was established in 1898, but back in the 1850s there was a tavern on the spot. In those Victorian times, the Swan Inn had a serious rival, which existed 13 doors away at Number 58 Wood Street, and this competing pub was a tavern known as the Ruthin Castle, run by a man named Joe Asbery, who tried all sorts of underhand tricks and devious antics to draw drinkers away from the Swan to his place. Drink-price wars between the two pubs erupted, but the clientele of the Swan remained remarkably loyal.

The Ruthin Castle had cheaper beverages, dirt-cheap mussels and occasionally free jellied eels but, even in Victorian times, the Swan Inn had a distinctive welcoming atmosphere and stronger ales than its rivals. At this time (in the 1850s,) the pub was managed by Ann Duncan, a very charismatic woman in her thirties who treated all the drinkers like family members.

Late one midsummer evening, around 1853, the Swan Inn was packed with drinkers, many of whom were dancing to an Irish band of musicians, when a window was smashed. Ann Duncan and several of the drinkers went outside and saw no one on Wood Street except a group of warehouse men harnessing horses at the far end of the thoroughfare, near Hanover Street. The only other figure that was noticed on this night was a drunken vagrant, and he was sitting in a doorway in the moonlight, almost opposite the pub.

Mrs Duncan went over to the tramp and asked him if he had thrown the stone and he admitted that he had, but it had been thrown with the best of intentions. Mrs Duncan was furious at the down-and-out's admission and asked him what he had been thinking about as he had smashed the pub window. The tramp said he had been aiming the stone at the 'witch' who had been writing something on the doorstep of the Swan. The scruffily-dressed Ishmaelite further explained that he knew the woman was a witch because she had jinxed him many years ago and caused his business to fail – the beginning of his downfall.

Ann Duncan and the gaggle of drinkers went to inspect the stone step in front of the Swan Inn and, sure enough, someone had chalked seven strange words upon it, and one of those words was 'Astaroth'.

One of the drinkers, tobacconist Jack Denman, said he possessed a smattering of knowledge concerning the occult, and believed the chalked words formed a curse invoking the demon Astaroth, one of the infamous 'Dukes of Hell' who inevitably caused havoc once he had been summoned up.

'Wash it off!' Mrs Duncan told her brother Robert, but Mr Denman advised the landlady not to do that, for washing such a 'witch-graffito' away was acknowledged to only make the invisible effects of the curse even harder to remove. Denman instead suggested that Mrs Duncan should seek 'wise counsel' from someone who knew how to remove such curses in a proper and effective manner. Mrs Duncan asked who could possibly do such a thing, and Denman said he knew of a man, a real-life warlock, who was well-versed in such arcane matters. His name was Patric Shalos (pronounced Shayloss), and he lived in a cottage in the district of Thingwall, over on Wirral.

'Oh, we shan't be needing someone like that,' said Mrs Duncan with a dismissive smirk, 'I'll tell a priest to bless the beer house instead.'

'This curse is from an ancient religion that was here long before Christianity,' Denman told the landlady, and many of the drinkers recoiled at the blasphemous assertions of the tobacconist.

'Fiddlesticks!' Mrs Duncan said, and she hurried away to fetch a sponge and a bucket of water. Mr Denman took out a pencil and piece of paper and scrawled down the seven strange words. Then the landlady came out and washed the cryptic message away. As she did so, the full moon slid behind a cloud, plunging badly-lit Wood Street into an eerie gloom, and in this darkness, the sounds of a dog howling could be heard somewhere in the distance.

'There, all the codswallop's gone now,' announced Mrs Duncan, wiping her hands on her pinafore. Then she stood up and, turning her back on the vagrant, marched back into the Swan Inn. A second later, she cried out and fell down unconscious.

When the landlady came to, she said someone had struck her on the back of the head but not one of the drinkers had been close enough to strike her as they entered the pub, although several of the regulars claimed they had heard the sound of something hitting Mrs Duncan.

Over the next few days, more strange incidents took

place in the Swan Inn. The ales began to taste sour, and the best and most expensive brandy began to smell like vinegar. Drinkers who went to the pub toilet found they couldn't stop urinating, and the Swan's cat, Shamrock, kept hissing at something in the bar that no human eyes could see.

There was a loud crash upstairs one evening, and Mrs Duncan found her best crockery lying in pieces on the floor. Then a plate sailed past her head and smashed against the wall. That same evening, one of the drinkers requested a glass of gin and, as Mrs Duncan tilted the bottle to pour the drink, the glass was seen to dart away a few inches and the gin spilled on to the counter.

A priest from St Peter's Church on Church Street was informed of the supernatural goings-on at the pub but condescendingly sneered at Mrs Duncan's account and suggested that the incidents could probably be put down to 'hallucinations from the bottle'. Mrs Duncan stormed away from the priest's residence and paid a visit to Jack Denman. She told him about the strange phenomena that was playing havoc with her business and humbly asked him to enlist the help of the 'warlock'.

On the following day, before dawn, Mr Denman travelled to Thingwall, and somehow managed to persuade Mr Shalos to accompany him back to Liverpool, where Mrs Duncan provided the Cheshire occultist with his own quarters and allowed him to drink and eat as much as he required during his stay. When Shalos arrived in a carriage at the Swan with Denman, Mrs Duncan noticed her rival, Joe Asbery, standing across the road, watching proceedings from under the brim of a wide felt hat.

Over breakfast, Patric Shalos surveyed the words of the chalked spell that Jack Denman had copied down. It

72

was a particularly nasty spell in his experience, and to countermand it he had brought along the esoteric tools of his trade in a satchel. Some of the requests Shalos subsequently made were met with bemused looks from both the landlady and her drinkers. He asked for hanging baskets to be hung on chains on either side of the entrance to the Swan, and this was done. Shalos then uprooted vervain plants in the wild fields of the suburbs and planted them in the hanging baskets. Vervain is a plant of great magical protection from evil, known as the 'tears of Isis' by the ancient Egyptians and was once traditionally gathered around the time of midsummer, when the star Sirius was prominent, and it was used to cleanse the altars of Jupiter in ancient Rome. Daughters of the Druids were also crowned with blue and purple vervain after initiation ceremonies. The ancient Picts also revered the juice of the plant as a healing ointment.

At noon, as the hanging baskets were being woven and the chains were being fastened to the walls of the pub, the front door of the Swan burst open, and a howling vortex of wind hurtled through the premises, overturning tables and chairs before blowing itself out. People cringed with fear, but the warlock Shalos told them it was just the work of desperate witches who were now angry because they knew their powers were being challenged and would soon be overcome.

Inside the Swan Inn, over the entrance of the door, Shalos drove a spike into the wall and attached a three-legged symbol known as the Triskelion, which we today would associate with the symbol of the Isle of Man. This powerful iron symbol hung in the Swan for many years, until it was removed around 1900 by Ada Allison, the landlady of the pub at that time. Following its removal, bad luck plagued Mrs Allison until the symbol was re-mounted. It has since been lost.

After the purple vervain had been put in the baskets, the warlock Shalos happened to glance over at the mirror behind the bar, and there he saw the faint ghostly vision of a pair of pale oval faces. They were of two women of about thirty, and their eyes resembled black almonds. They both scowled as the warlock looked on. Jack Denman followed the magician's line of sight and saw what he was looking at. 'The witches?' he whispered, and Shalos nodded. The faces quickly vanished. Shalos had the mirror covered up with a sheet of tarpaulin, and explained to Mrs Duncan how a looking-glass could be used as a spying-glass by certain witches who practised the Dark Arts.

The next plan was to identify the witches if at all possible, and once their names had been discovered, there were two courses of action: to either kill them, or banish them. Shalos preferred to kill the witches, as in his experience, Hell had no fury like a witch who had suffered the humiliation of banishment and he told Denman how a coven of blackballed witches had managed to overcome a banishment ritual to kill a warlock on Thor's Stone on Thurstaston Common in Wirral. This stone, which is over 230 million years old, is still used by real witches today. 'If you kill them you'll be hanged,' Jack Denman warned Shalos, but the warlock shook his head and said the bodies of the witches would never be found after he had finished with them. 'I won't help you to murder women, witches or not,' Denman said sombrely.

'What's all this talk of murder?' asked Mrs Duncan, as she approached the table. Shalos then explained the two choices as to the treatment of the witches, and

74

Mrs Duncan said, 'No, you can't kill anybody, Patric. All I require is to keep the witches from my door.'

Shalow and Denman tried to discover who the witches were and even went in disguise into the Ruthin Castle tavern in an effort to eavesdrop on the conversation of the landlord Joe Asbery, but the strangers, being outsiders, soon aroused suspicion among the regulars and were told to leave.

The unexpected break came from Mrs Duncan, who told Shalos about the tramp who had smashed the window of her pub as he tried to throw a stone at the witch who had scrawled the spell on the doorstep. The vagrant had recognised the witch as the woman who had jinxed his business years before. The vagrant was traced a few days later, and brought to the Swan Inn, where Shalos and Mrs Duncan quizzed him over the witch who had chalked the malevolent spell.

The vagrant, whose name was Morris, said the witch was not known to him by name, only by sight, and four years ago she was living with her sister in Wolstenholme Square at the end of Parr Street. Mrs Duncan promised the tramp five shillings if he would show Mr Shalos where the 'witches' lived. The vagrant cheerily agreed to the offer and, under the cover of night, Patric Shalos, Jack Denman, and the tramp Morris loitered in the shadows of the trees in the park that was situated in the centre of Wolstenholme Square. The vagrant squinted at the motley row of lamp-lit houses and warehouses before pointing at a thin dark-bricked terraced dwelling. 'I think that's the house there. I'd say I'm sure of it in fact,' he added.

It was fast approaching midnight and the three men waited for a while as three old stragglers, all old men, stood talking on a corner nearby. Judging by the way the trio were swaying, they'd just returned from a tavern. Then each bid the other goodnight as a clock chimed midnight, and when the last one had gone into his home, Shalos walked alone to the house that the vagrant had pointed out. He stooped upon reaching the three stone steps and took a small strong-bladed knife from his belt. He engraved something on the top step with the point of the knife, and moments afterwards, a policeman entered the square, heading in the direction of the self-proclaimed warlock. Jack Denman instructed the vagrant to stay behind the tree, and not to move an inch. The tobacconist then started yelling, 'Police! Stop thief!' before he ran off pell mell out of the square.

'What is it?' the policeman shouted over to the retreating figure. Denman stopped, and gestured for the policeman to follow him with a wind-milling motion of his left arm. 'I've been robbed!' Denman shouted, 'and he ran off down here!'

Patric Shalos, meanwhile, finished etching his powerful spell into the doorstep. Any witch within that dwelling would now be housebound. Unless she had someone to bring her food or water, the witch would now die of thirst or hunger, and sometimes, if the witch happened to be asleep at the time when the spell was cast, she would remain asleep, as if in a coma.

The policeman suddenly realised that Denman was merely trying to distract him and refused to follow the tobacconist any further. He turned to see Shaloss slide a knife back into a sheath on his belt as he walked away from the house. That naturally struck the officer as suspicious, and so he gripped the handle of his truncheon and challenged the stranger. 'You! Stay where you are!' he shouted.

76

Shalos did as he was bid, and turned to face him. 'I've done no wrong sir,' he told the policeman.

'You have a knife there,' said the policeman, 'have you just used it?'

Shalos gazed into the policeman's intense dark eyes, then probed his logical but limited mind and easily took control of it. He reached out and placed his thumb between those eyes, at the top of the officer's nose, and the lawman's eyes gently closed.

Shalos walked away to join the other two on Parr Street, and when they looked back, the policeman was still standing there in the square, as stock-still as a statue. The witches were never heard from again and their malign influence was permanently lifted from the Swan Inn. They say that Joe Asbery, the landlord of the Ruthin Castle, brought the witches food and drink at first and tried to remove them from the house on Wolstenholme Square, but it proved to be impossible, for the sisters experienced agonising pains as soon as they tried to leave the house. There was talk many years later of two skeletons in tattered clothes, with nests of rats in their rib-cages being found in a derelict house in Wolstenholme Square.

The Swan Inn thrived, Joe Asbery died, and the Ruthin Castle closed down for good when its customers deserted it. Shalos lived at the Swan Inn for many years as an honoured guest, and during his stay, Mrs Duncan prospered well.

A Midnight Race of Death

One summer night in the 1980s, a biker from the Swan Inn got into a friendly argument with a biker from Dino's, a club close to the Swan that was often frequented by motorcyclists. Mick, the biker who was a regular at the Swan, said he was a better rider than Tod, the Dino's biker, and furthermore, he maintained that his gleaming machine was much faster. Tod therefore challenged Mick to a race and set out the circuit. They were to ride to the top of Wood Street, turn right into Berry Street, straight down Great George Street and on to Upper Parliament Street, along the dock road (Chaloner Street, Wapping and the Strand), before turning right up James Street. From there the bikers would have to take a big risk by flouting the traffic system and travelling the wrong way down one-way streets and so on to get back to Wood Street.

The two competing bikers were fuelled to the eyeballs with heavy liquor and didn't give a damn about the potential consequences for themselves or anyone else at the time. As a huge crowd of onlookers from the Swan, Dino's and a club called Freewheelers gathered to watch, the bikers waited for a signal from a bouncer, who was staring at his watch with his hand raised. The second finger was crawling towards midnight, and the bouncer began the countdown: 'Five … four … three … two … one!' The bikers tore off up Wood Street on their insane mission with the engines of their bikes roaring like a pride of lions. Off they went into the night, trying to outmanoeuvre and outdistance each other through Chinatown, even jumping a red light near the Blackie, which almost resulted in a head-on collision with a juggernaut.

The crowd outside the Swan waited for Tod and Mick to return and some of the drinkers even placed bets on who would arrive first. At twenty minutes past midnight, there should have been some sign of the reckless duo, but they were still nowhere to be seen. At around half-past midnight, the silhouette of a solitary motorbike with a dull headlamp appeared at the Hanover Street end of Wood Street, and cheers went up in the crowd. It looked like Mick from the Swan, but then more bikes appeared at the end of the street, massing behind the biker whom everyone assumed to be Mick, but not one of these motorcycles made any noise.

The crowd squinted at the convoy of night-riders coming up the gloomy street, and when the bikers drew near enough, people saw they were all strangers, dressed in leather jackets that were not, strangely, emblazoned with badges and nor did their helmets bear any logos, stickers, or any sort of design. The silent leader of the motorcycle gang had no visor on his crash helmet, and his face was as white as chalk. Members of the crowd quickly sensed that there was something deeply sinister about the rider, and they jumped out of the way because his bike showed no signs of slowing down. He passed the Swan Inn as he rolled through the crowd, and it looked as if he was free-wheeling because there was no sound at all from his bike, not even any noise from the tread of his tyres on the cold macadam of the road.

Six more unknown bikers followed, and their machines were all silent too and their faces were just as pale as the leading motorcyclist. Then something quite bizarre happened. The head biker performed a wheelie, and sped up Wood Street with his front wheel high in the air, and he, and the other six bikers, one after the other, slowly faded away as the crowd gasped in astonishment.

Len Challis, one of the older drinkers, grabbed the arm of a girl punk-rocker, and seemed unsteady on his feet all of a sudden. The teenager asked him if he was okay, and Challis told her something that eventually spread through the crowd.

'They used to be the Chain Gang,' the middle-aged man whispered, nodding towards the top of the street, where the spectres of the motorcyclists had just faded into nothingness. To those who would listen, and many did bend their ear to his claims that night, the former biker said the Chain Gang was a motley collection of riders from across the North West who had been active in the 1950s and 1960s, around the same time as another local bike-riding gang called the War Pigs. But Challis knew for a fact that time, hard-drinking, a succession of accidents and serious illnesses had caught up with most of the members of the Chain Gang, and only two of that nine-strong crew were still alive.

The old biker expressed the opinion that the ghostly procession of motor bikers had actually been an omen of death, and this dark speculation was soon proved to be true, for some tragic news arrived later that night: Tod and Mick had crashed into one another on the dock road and smashed into a wall. Tod had been killed outright and Mick was hospitalised with serious head-injuries for months.

A white cross was later painted on the wall at the scene of the death-crash by the leader of a gang of bikers out of respect. It subsequently came to light that Tod's late father had been a member of the Chain Gang, and had been a regular at the Swan Inn in the 1960s.

Tell Him I Love Him

A few years after the time of the last tale, in the mid-1980s, a 19-year-old girl with the unusually spelt first name of Czoey (with the Cz pronounced as in the word Czar) was walking up Hope Street one blisteringly sunny Saturday afternoon from her flat on Mount Street, when she noticed a smartly-dressed young black lad of about 13, standing on the steps of an old Georgian house. The teenager smiled at Czoey Lang as she passed by, and the girl just knew there was something strange about him, but couldn't put her finger on it, and as she turned to look back, the youth walked straight through the solid closed door of the house.

Czoey had seen a ghost that many people have reported to me over the years, and the house concerned was a club which went under several names during various incarnations, including the name, Chauffeurs. It is thought that the apparition in question was that of a young trainee butler, who died from a fever on the premises of the Hope Street dwelling in the late nineteenth century.

Czoey was startled by the ghost's passing through the closed door, but she had seen such things before. The girl was undoubtedly psychic, as was her mother and grandmother before her, and such unearthly traits are often passed on in families through the female line down the generations. She continued on her way down Hope Street and turned left down Leece Street on her way to the Swan Inn on Wood Street, where she hoped to see her friend Marella Feldon. Like Czoey, Marella was a Liverpool University student, and both girls hailed from Leeds but had not known each other until they arrived in Liverpool.

When Czoey went into the Swan, she saw, to her dismay, that Marella wasn't there. Marella was a Goth, and often walked about barefooted in black wedding gowns with dark purple hair. She was just one of the many unorthodox people who seemed to gravitate towards the pub, and there were many more unusual but entertaining characters in the Wood Street watering hole on that sizzling summer afternoon.

Czoey looked around; there was a man who went around with a contented-looking cat that was constantly perched on his shoulder, a man in combat jacket and matching camouflage-patterned trousered who took a stuffed bird out of his pocket now and then and inspected it closely now and then for some bizarre reason, and now a girl of around eighteen had just entered the pub dressed like something from the 1960s. She wore red white and blue striped tights, and a knee-length yellow dress with daisies printed on it. The girl had a bob of shiny red hair, a freckled elfin face, and elaborate eye make up which gave the impressions of spirals around her eyes.

The girl smiled at Czoey and said something which the juke box drowned out, so Czoey picked up her lager and lime, and went over to the retro-attired girl. 'Sorry, what was that?' she said, and angled her right ear towards the younger girl, who smiled and shook her head because of the futility of attempting a conversation with a jukebox booming at such high amplitude. The freckled girl backed away and beckoned Czoey to follow her outside.

The girls stepped outside the Swan and sat at a small round walnut tea table that had been put their for the alfresco drinkers on such an infernal day. 'I couldn't hear a word you were saying there, sorry,' Czoey remarked.

'I was just asking if you'd seen Chris by any chance?' replied the girl.

Czoey didn't know that many people in the Swan yet, as she'd only been going to the pub for a few weeks, and she certainly didn't know anyone named Chris, so she shook her head.

'He looks like Jim Morrison,' the red-headed teen told Czoey, 'and he always wears a red carnation in his lapel; you probably know him by sight.'

'I'm sorry,' said Czoey, 'but he doesn't sound like anyone I know. Who's John Morrison?'

'Jim,' said the pretty stranger, and beamed a contagious smile, 'Jim Morrison, you know, the Doors?'

'Oh!' said Czoey, none the wiser.

'Hey, can I get you a drink?' she asked the girl.

'No, it's okay, I have to shoot off soon,' she replied.

'Just one,' Czoey asked, 'because I don't want to sit out here on my own like a saddo.'

The girl laughed and said, 'Alright, I'll have a sarsaparilla, with a straw if you can.'

Czoey Lang had never heard of a sarsaparilla but she went and ordered one anyway, and got herself a half pint of cider and blackcurrant. The barman said no one drank sarsaparilla any more, and said the nearest he had to that drink was a Pepsi. Czoey went back outside and put the glass of Pepsi with a red and white striped barber-pole straw before the redhead.

'They didn't have sarsaparilla so I had to get a Pepsi,' Czoey said, and the girl smiled and said, 'That's fine, thanks very much.'

The two teenagers got talking, and the girl told Czoey her name was Harry, short for Harriet. She worked in the

Thomas Cook travel agency on Bold Street but today was her day off and she'd hoped to see her boyfriend Chris in the Swan because she'd had a silly argument with him and hadn't talked to him for ages. 'I really miss him,' Harry said, and all of a sudden she buried her face in her hands and started to sob.

'Hey, are you okay?' Czoey asked, and she reached out and put her hand on the girl's shoulder. 'You'll see him again if he comes in here, Harry, don't cry.'

Harry wiped her tears with the back of her hand and the spirals drawn with an eyeliner pen around her eyes were a bit smudged now.

'I'm sorry,' she said.

'Don't apologise,' Czoey told her, 'I've been in the same sort of situation in the past. You'll see Chris again, I promise.'

'Well, just in case I don't, can you do me a favour?' Harry suddenly asked.

'You'll see him again, you're bound to …' Czoey was saying.

'Yes, but can you do me a favour if you see him first?' Harry persisted, and there was desperation in her voice and eyes now.

Czoey forced a smile and said: 'I don't even know what he looks like, though.'

Harry sniffled. 'Well, if you see a lad who looks like Jim Morrison and has a red carnation in his lapel, can you tell him I still love him so much?'

'Yeah, okay,' Czoey said, and she heard the pad of flip flops approaching from her right. She turned to see her friend Marella approaching in a pair of ridiculously large sunglasses.

'Don't tell me you're actually trying to catch a tan

with that much foundation on,' Marella said to her friend, and then adjusted her sunglasses so that her smiling brown eyes peeped over the top of them.

'Marella, this is Harry,' Czoey said, gesturing towards the girl with her left hand. Marella shot back a puzzled look in her brown eyes. Czoey turned in her chair to see that Harry had gone. Just an untouched glass of Pepsi remained on the table with its striped straw to prove that the girl had not been a figment of Czoey's imagination.

It slowly dawned on Czoey that Harry had been a ghost; another of those eerie visitants who kept running into her, but she couldn't tell Marella that.

The normal psychically-myopic people of this world couldn't take in the notion of a society of spirits living in parallel with the diurnal society of living and breathing folk. In a hundred years perhaps they might accept the concept, but not in 1985.

'I never saw anyone sitting with you, and I was looking over at you from the corner up there, talking to a friend,' Marella said, feeling a bit unnerved by Czoey's strange behaviour.

'She must have left when my back was turned,' Czoey said, thinking fast on her feet, 'because she did say she had to go somewhere.'

'I thought you said his name was Harry?' said Marella feeling more confused by the minute.

'No, her name's Harriet, but she gets called Harry,' explained Czoey, and she rose from the table and asked Marella what she would like to drink as they both went into the Swan.

About an hour later, Czoey was returning from the toilet in the Swan when she happened to pass a middle-aged man on the stairs. What made her notice him was the fact that he wore a red carnation in his lapel. She wondered if he might be Chris, Harry's boyfriend. Czoey knew she should have just walked on past the grey-haired man, but she stopped and said to him, 'Excuse me, is your name Chris by any chance?'

The man regarded Czoey with a suspicious eye, and answered, 'Yeah, why?' Czoey wondered how to convey the message from a girl who had probably been dead for a very long time, if her sixties-styled clothes were anything to go by.

'Harry told me to pass this message on,' Czoey said, awkwardly. 'She told me to tell you that she still loves you very much.'

Chris seemed to freeze for a few seconds and then a tear welled up in the inner corner of his left eye.

'Did you actually see her?' he asked, and the tear meandered down his cheek and on to his top lip. He brushed it away with his knuckle.

'Yes, I saw her today,' Czoey said, and described her clothes, her unusual eye make-up, and as she did so, Chris began to smile, even though tears continued to fall.

'That's Harry alright,' Chris said, but could hardly get his words out because he was so choked up. 'Are you some kind of medium? You must be; other people have seen her now and then; I know she's still around.'

Czoey nodded, 'I suppose I am a medium of sorts, except I don't charge for my services or anything like that.' She had a question. 'I hope you don't mind me asking, Chris, but how did Harry pass away?'

Chris rummaged in his pocket and found an old crumpled hankie and with it he wiped the rain of tears from his agonised eyes and blew his nose into it.

'I killed her,' he whispered. Czoey unconsciously

stepped back from Chris, stunned by his words.

'It's okay, it's okay, there's no need to worry, I should have phrased that answer better that's all,' Chris said with a faint smile. 'We didn't know Harry had a bad heart and, well, I started seeing this other girl, and erm …' Chris wiped his eyes and his nose with the handkerchief again before he continued. 'I was walking down this street, funnily enough, when Harry bumped into me and the girl I was seeing, and er, she sort of slid down the wall. She looked at me with this funny expression as if she just couldn't believe I was with another girl and then she closed her eyes. She was dead by the time they got her to the hospital. They said it was her heart; that it was some sort of genetic defect, but I felt as if I had killed her.'

'I'm so sorry,' Czoey said, and she watched Chris sob like a baby.

He looked up with bloodshot eyes and a face smeared with tears. 'If, if you see her again, please tell her I love her. '

'I will. Are you okay?' Czoey asked, full of concern for the guilt-ridden forty-year-old.

'Yes, I'll be okay. I feel better in a way now that you told me she still loves me,' said Chris.

When Marella came into the passageway and saw Czoey talking to the crying man, she became concerned, and shouted over to her. 'Czoey are you alright?'

'Yeah, I'm just going to powder my nose then I'll be with you!' Czoey shouted back, then went back to the toilet.

By 7pm, Marella and Czoey had had more than enough to drink, and as they sat outside the Swan, they both decided they should call it a day, even though it was so early. They were just gathering their things together when a young man with long black hair arrived on a Harley Davidson motorcycle and pulled up outside the pub. Marella whispered into Czoey's ear. 'That lad on the bike's called Chris. Don't you think he's gorgeous. I really fancy the pants off him.'

Czoey burst into laughter and looked at the young biker in his black leather jacket, Levi 501s and boots and he gazed back at her through his visor, then winked. His hair hung down below his shoulders, and as he took off his helmet, Marella said, 'Wow, look at those sideburns; I love a man with sideys.'

Marella had to go to the toilet, and when she came back, she found the man of her dreams chatting up Czoey outside the Swan. She was green with envy, and she deliberately interrupted the conversation by saying, 'Come on Czoe! We've got to get you home, girl. You're totally wrecked.'

Chris just laughed and asked Czoey if she'd like a lift home on his Harley. This made Marella even more jealous and she physically dragged Czoey away from the handsome biker. As the two tipsy young women reached the top of the street, Czoey spotted Harry standing in a doorway, smiling at her. Czoey stopped and, in a slurred voice, she said, 'I gave your message to Chris, and he said he loves you.'

The ghost smiled, softly closed her eyes with a blissful expression, and placed her hands on her chest and then melted away into the evening air.

'Thank you, Czoey,' came a faint echoing reply from somewhere beyond this world.

'What do you mean … you gave my message to Chris?' Marella asked, stopping in her tracks. She tried to remain still but her legs wobbled, she was in such a state of intoxication. Then she continued; 'And what do you mean by saying he loves me? He hardly even knows me, though I wish he did.'

Of course, Marella hadn't seen Harry, and had presumed Czoey had been talking to her instead about the lad on the bike.

'Er, yes, you may think you hardly know him, Marella, but Chris certainly seems to know you,' Czoey lied, rather than risk losing a friend who might possibly abandon her if she knew she talked to spirits.

'You're not just saying that, are you, Czoe?' Marella asked, leaning heavily on Czoey's arm, and they both stumbled and fell on to the pavement, laughing till their sides hurt.

THE OLD POST OFFICE
School Lane

Far removed from the hectic kaleidoscopic bustle of Liverpool life, off the beaten track of the main arterial thoroughfares of the city, you will find a sanctum from the rat race in the Old Post Office public house, which stands on the corner where Old Post Office Place (which once ran from Church Street) meets School Lane, a mere stone's throw from the Bluecoat Chambers. This atmospheric pub was named after a post office which stood on the spot from 1800 to 1839. There have been many supernatural goings-on at the Old Post Office, from Victorian times up to the present day, in fact, but let us start in chronological order.

Secrets From the Other Side

In late October 1890, a westering autumn sun hung low over Wirral, sending shafts of golden light down School Lane. The jaundiced rays of the dying day filtered through the translucent arabesque swirls etched upon the frosted panes of the corner door of the Old Post Office tavern, where the 35-year-old pub licensee Edward 'Eddy' John Shadrach leaned on the counter, watching the various illegal card games taking place around the bar – not that anyone batted an eyelid at them, especially since Detective Inspector Irvine was known to join in from time to time. Eddy Shadrach had told the gamblers and card-sharps that he didn't approve of their felonious activities, and when the licensee complained to a Detective Sergeant Jackson about the gamblers, he had been told, 'Sir, we can't manage your house for you, so take them by the scruffs of their necks and throw them out if you find them disagreeable.' But many of these gamblers were hard men, and most belonged to notorious gangs and street-wise syndicates, and by no stretch of the imagination could Eddy Shadrach take them by the 'scruffs of their necks' and throw them off his premises, so he eventually resigned himself to the situation.

Meanwhile, upstairs in the Old Post Office pub, very strange proceedings were taking place in a darkened room. Lizzy Gilluly, the older, widowed sister of Eddy Shadrach, stood in a trance, surrounded by an engrossed circle of sharply-attired men of distinction, some with notebooks, who scribbled down the words spouted by the tall, willowy 38-year-old beauty, as if she was some latter-day Delphic Oracle.

Since her childhood, Lizzy had displayed the psychic talents of clairvoyancy, and what is known in occult circles as 'direct voice' ability – a faculty by which the medium speaks in the actual voices of the dead, and over the years, news of her strange powers had finally reached the ears of the upper classes.

Upon this autumn evening, Lizzy Gilluly spoke first in an oriental-sounding tongue that the sitters could not understand, so one of the distinguished gentlemen present, who was said to be a close associate of the eminent physicist and spiritualism-researcher, Sir Oliver Lodge, asked the entity speaking through the Liverpool woman to talk in English. The entity obliged, and explained that he had lived in a carnate body in Liverpool's Chinatown until fifteen years ago, when he had died of tuberculosis. At one point in the conversation from beyond the grave, the spirit of the Chinaman said: 'All that we are arises with our thoughts. With our thoughts we make the world. Speak or act with an impure mind and trouble will follow you, as the wheel follows the ox that draws the cart.'

In the middle of the disembodied Buddhist discourse, Lizzy suddenly began to talk in a raspy, menacing voice, as a substance resembling green smoke began to accumulate above her head. 'Good evenin' to you all, me name's Larty.' The men of the circle, young and old, recoiled in horrified surprise as the green vapour condensed into a globe, about a foot in diameter, with a hideous grinning face upon it. Monocles dropped, followed by gasps of shock, and the sound of chairs scraping their legs across the floor as the sitters backed away from the fiendish spherical face.

'You have nothing to fear but the truth,' 'Larty'

announced, 'and I am here to bring the truth to light! A secret or two to be revealed!'

'Turn on the light!' an elderly doctor called out, rising to his feet, but a young businessman disagreed, and said such sudden illumination would be downright dangerous and possibly life-threatening to the medium. As the nervous doctor stumbled towards the door, a serious student of spiritualism, with the unusual surname of Stirzaker, seized him by the arm and told him to 'face the unknown', but the doctor violently tore his arm from the man's grip and left the room, leaving the door ajar. The well known and respected physician, who ministered to many of Liverpool's most influential families, was so overwhelmed with fear that he left his coat, top-hat, cape and walking cane behind – and never returned for them.

The globular-headed apparition laughed loudly and shouted to his departing back, 'The good doctor isn't really so good! Methinks he is afraid of what I may reveal about him! He keeps a mistress as young as his grand-daughter!'

This shocking revelation caused some of the remaining eight sitters to become very uneasy. What was this thing which had so rudely intruded upon their seance? A demon?

'Mr Fairbanks!' said the grass-green ball of mischief to a well-known florist. 'Where is your beloved partner? Is he writing a sermon tonight? You do make a pretty couple … a Darby and John!'

Upon which Mr Fairbanks made the sign of the cross and hastily left the room saying, 'This is all lies and trickery!'

The apparition apparently thought this hilarious and faded away into the shadows as he guffawed with laughter, leaving the sitters in complete disarray. Most of them left almost immediately, but two middle-aged men of clear conscience remained to attend to Lizzy Gilluly as she emerged from her trance in tears. She could remember nothing, but told them she felt frightened and sad. Later that night, she showed her younger brother Eddy Shadrach the one hundred guineas she had made, and told him what she had done to earn the payment, and he advised his sister to stop dabbling with the supernatural and to begin attending church again. Lizzy agreed. She relayed to him what the sitters had told her about the trouble-causing spirit, Larty, and how he seemed to know everyone's darkest secrets and to delight in making them known to the assembled company. Eddy became very nervous, and warned his sister that such knowledge was a very dangerous thing, and that people in power might even resort to trying to kill her for revealing their secrets.

A week went by, and one rainy evening a fine-looking carriage came trundling down School Lane and halted in front of the Old Post Office. The faces of drinkers fired with curiosity peered through the panes of the pub window at the illustrious visitor who alighted from the carriage. He wore a topper, a long opera cloak, and in his white gloved hands he carried an expensive-looking walking cane. When this gentleman entered the pub, he was seen to have bushy white sideburns and a pair of piercing sapphire-blue eyes. To Mr Shadrach, the licensee of the establishment, he asked in a rough deep voice: 'Where is Elizabeth Gilluly?'

'Why? Who's asking?' was Eddy Shadrach's reply, and the well-heeled stranger, ignoring the question, walked up to the landlord and enquired if Mrs Gilluly was in.

A tall, thickset warehouseman named McNamee rose from a stool in the corner of the pub and swaggered across to the counter. 'Answer the man,' McNamee said, addressing the stranger. 'Tell him who you are.'

At this point the drinkers and Shadrach discovered that the stranger's walking cane was, in fact, a sword-stick, when the top-hatted visitor drew a gleaming deadly-looking blade from the sheath of the cane and in a heartbeat pressed its tip against McNamee's chest. A policeman came into the pub named Frank Bellringer, a bobby whom Shadrach knew well, for he usually called into the pub after midnight during his School Lane beat. Bellringer immediately took in the scene, focusing on the blade held threateningly against the warehouseman's chest, and Shadrach asked the policeman to escort the belligerent gentleman from the premises.

But PC Bellringer said nothing, and the arrogant stranger turned to him and simply said, 'Go.' PC Bellringer left the pub without uttering a word, and all of the drinkers looked at one another with baffled expressions. Who was this stranger who could even dictate to the law?

The door behind the bar suddenly creaked open, and out came Lizzy Gilluly.

'Ah! Are you Elizabeth Gilluly?' the enigmatic visitor asked.

'No, she isn't!' said Eddy Shadrach.

But simultaneously, his sister answered: 'Yes, why do you ask sir?'

'If you try to take my sister from here, we'll tear you to pieces,' the landlord threatened, but the visitor smiled and coolly beckoned with his free hand for Lizzy to accompany him. The door of the pub steadily opened, and everyone turned to see who was entering except the stranger, probably because he knew it was his back-up. A bearded man in a dark brown Ulster coat and a black bowler entered, and in his hand he carried a revolver. One of the old soldiers in the bar recognised the gun as an Adams Mark III – standard issue in the British Army many years ago. The interloper with the sword-stick escorted Lizzy outside, while the man with the pistol surveyed the drinkers until his colleague and the abducted woman were safely inside the carriage, and he then joined them. The driver of the coach gently jerked on the reins and the carriage moved off in heavy a downpour with a few of the drinkers trotting behind it as far as Hanover Street.

Half an hour after this, a joiner named Jack Ivinson came into the Old Post Office, soaked to the skin, and after ordering rum, he said he had seen Lizzy Gilluly leave a 'well-to-do coach', flanked by two men, about twenty minutes ago. The men had led Lizzy into a house on Rodney Street, but Jack wasn't sure which one. Eddy Shadrach asked Jack if he would show him which houses the men might have taken Lizzy into, but the joiner protested that he was soaked to the skin and already catching his death, and really didn't want to get involved, and besides, he and the other drinkers were very curious to know exactly what Shadrach's sister had been abducted for anyway. What was so special about her?

The licensee didn't want to broadcast his sister's mediumistic abilities for fear of ridicule, and so he left the pub clutching a pistol and went to find Lizzy himself. Shadrach called at several houses on Rodney Street, but was turned away from them by various servants until a PC George Copeland (256 E) noticed the pub licensee arguing with a butler and footman at Number 72 Rodney Street – the house of respected physician, James Barr. PC Copeland told Shadrach to go home, dismissing his story about the abduction of his sister 'a lie'.

Lizzy Gilluly was dropped off at the Old Post Office pub at four in the morning by a hansom cab, and she was in a dreadful state. At that hour, her brother was still up fretting about her and had a number of drinkers with him for company in the pub. Lizzy said that she had been warned by a mysterious man named Keel that she would disappear without a trace if she ever used her 'witchery' again. Lizzy had gained the distinct impression that she had been seen as posing a threat to someone high up in society with her powers; that she had possibly already exposed them and brought a scandal to light, and she felt that she was lucky – so far - to have escaped with her life.

Eddy Shadrach refused to take the hint from the mysterious Mr Keel, and tried to lodge a complaint against him – even though he wasn't sure exactly where on Rodney Street Lizzy had been taken to – and he soon realised that he was up against someone who could even influence the forces of law and order.

Detectives repeatedly called at the Old Post Office and inspected the cellars, saying they had received tip-offs about the storage of stolen goods. Then plain-clothed detectives started visiting the pub to monitor the illegal gambling, and Lizzy Gilully received menacing letters from Mr Keel, telling her that she and her brother were being watched around the clock, and that their graves had already been dug in a certain cellar.

By the summer of 1891, a full-scale police surveillance operation was in full swing, and scared away many of the drinkers at the Old Post Office pub. On 14 August Eddy

Shadrach was summonsed to appear before Mr J H Kinghorn, the Stipendiary Magistrate at Liverpool Police Court, and charged with allowing his premises to be used for gambling. 'That he had knowingly and wilfully permitted his premises to be used for betting' was how the prosecutors put it.

Eddy Shadrach shouted: 'The police are very sharp now, aren't they? But when I appealed to them many times for protection, pleading with them to turn these betting men away, I was told they could not manage my house for me!'

A Detective Sergeant Jackson then produced two small betting books to the court and said with a smile that he had found these incriminating pieces of evidence under manager Shadrach's coat, as well as three racing calendars in a drawer. Mr Berry, defending Shadrach, asked Jackson if the handwriting in the racing books was anything like his client's. Jackson was begrudgingly forced to admit that he couldn't identify the handwriting as belonging to the pub manager. All of the police witnesses admitted in a roundabout way that they had not seen Eddy Shadrach actually put on the bets or make them. Nevertheless, Eddy Shadrach was heavily fined and almost had his license removed. He appealed against the decision in October 1891, but the appeal was dismissed, and Shadrach also had to pay additional court costs. He was then hounded by the police and several health inspectors until Lizzy Gilluly moved from the area and disappeared into obscurity.

What dark and grave secrets Lizzy's powers had touched upon in the upper echelons of society will probably never be known now, but there is a warning there: the genuine medium who really can contact the dead may unearth many old secrets that are better left buried.

Eddy Shadrach kept a low profile in later years and from 1910 to 1915 he was the manager of his last pub, Ye Cracke, on 13 Rice Street, off Hope Street.

What Did He See?

In 1902, the Old Post Office public house was being run by 50-year-old Staffordshire man, Thomas Henshaw, along with his 46-year-old wife Annie, who hailed from North Wales. The Henshaws had moved into the pub just a few years before, and everyone who knew them perceived them as a loving couple who ran the pub efficiently and always made their customers feel welcome.

In September 1902, a Welshman named Peter Morgan arrived at the Old Post Office, wanting to see the landlord's wife Annie. A barmaid named Rose asked him why he wanted to see Mrs Henshaw, and Morgan thumped his fist on the bar counter and barked, 'Just go and get her, woman!' Mr Henshaw was out at the time, and so Rose informed Annie of the aggressive visitor with the strong Welsh accent who was asking for her, and Mrs Henshaw came down immediately to see Morgan. Rose noticed the blood drain from Annie Henshaw's face when she first saw the caller, then watched as Annie showed Mr Morgan upstairs.

Annie claimed he was a relative, and at first she stuck to the same story when her husband returned to the pub, but then Morgan suddenly said, 'No, Annie, tell the truth. You can't go wrong when you tell the truth.'

Annie became tearful and bowed her head. Peter Morgan was a former lover of hers, and now he had arrived in Liverpool, looking for work, and wondered if Annie, or her husband, could possibly help him to find accommodation until he found employment. Tom Henshaw was a bit disappointed in his wife at first for lying to him about Morgan being a relative, but then he realised that she had only lied because she didn't want to hurt him by opening up her past with Morgan. Annie assured him that there was nothing between her and Morgan, and that she had left him when she was just a teenager, and in front of her old flame she told Tom she loved only him and that she would remain loyal to him until the day she died.

Tom Henshaw reluctantly let Peter Morgan stay in one of the two spare rooms upstairs in the pub, on the condition that he looked for work each day, and that he would accomplish the task of finding a job within a week.

'I promise you, you won't even know I'm here,' Morgan told Mr Henshaw, but this turned out to be a pie-crust promise, meant to be broken.

Morgan seemed to spend more time loafing in the bar than actively seeking work, so Tom Henshaw would sit him in the corner of the pub without a drink, and place a copy of the *Liverpool Mercury*, opened at the 'Situations Vacant' page.

Around this time, a mysterious rapping sound was heard each night, coming from the empty room next door to the one where Morgan was staying. Tom and Annie heard it at 1.20am as they lay in bed. Annie and her husband were enjoying their slumbers after working at the pumps from eight in the morning till 11pm, when suddenly they both awoke to the tapping noise. 'What's he up to now?' Tom asked, automatically assuming that the unwanted lodger Morgan was up to no good. He lit a candle, put on his slippers, left the room, then crept along the landing to the staircase and slowly climbed up, avoiding the two creaky steps. On the next landing, he saw Morgan's door slowly open, and his lodger's long sharp nose emerge from behind the doorframe.

'What are you doing, eh?' Tom Henshaw asked, startling Morgan.

'Sweet Jesus! You gave me a start then,' Morgan whispered, placing his hand on his chest. 'I'm not doing anything,' he said, 'I came out to see where that bleedin' noise is coming from; it's keeping me awake.'

'Priceless!' exclaimed Mr Henshaw, 'You're a veritable Henry Irving you are, Mr Morgan, acting all innocent. Come on, what're you up to?'

'I give you my word, Tom, I'm not …' Morgan began.

'Don't call me Tom, it's Mr Henshaw to you,' the landlord replied.

The tapping noise started up again, and both men heard it and looked at the door of the empty room.

Morgan looked back at Henshaw. 'See? Didn't I tell you it wasn't me? Someone's in there!'

'There's no one in there,' Henshaw told the Welsh lodger, but he seemed very nervous and unsure of his opinion. 'That door's been locked since I moved in here, and the only way in is through the window. A burglar would have to be Spring-Heeled Jack to get in there.'

'Well someone's in there alright,' said Morgan, and he put his ear against the door of the empty room, then stooped to look through the keyhole, but the keyhole was blocked with what looked like hardened putty. 'The keyhole's been plugged up. Why would someone do that?' said Morgan, and he scratched at the blockage with his fingernail.

'Leave it alone. It's probably rats,' said Henshaw. 'I'll get the vermin catcher out in the morning, now get back to bed, Mr Morgan, and stay there.'

'Must be a right big rat, Mr Henshaw,' Morgan muttered as he went back into his room.

Henshaw waited by the door to the empty room for a while longer, and heard no more noises, so he returned to his bed, and he and his wife slept soundly until morning.

On the following night, around midnight, a loud moan came from upstairs, and this time the Henshaws and Morgan as well as another couple, surnamed Wilson who had been allowed to stay behind for a drink and a chat, heard the strange sound. The Wilsons looked at one another, startled, then Mr Wilson said, 'What on earth was that?'

'I'll go and see,' volunteered Peter Morgan, and he lifted the counter flap and went through the open doorway to the stairs.

'It sounded like a cat that's got trapped somewhere,' was Mr Henshaw's feeble explanation, and he quickly added, 'Sound can play funny tricks at night, believe me. I've stood at the Pier Head at night and heard a man coughing over in Birkenhead. The river amplifies any sound at night when everything's still.'

The Wilsons gazed up at the ceiling, listening to the thudding footfalls of Morgan as he climbed up the stairs. Minutes went by, and there was still no word from Morgan. Mr Henshaw began to worry about the Welshman spending so much time upstairs unsupervised, and wondered if he might be snooping around in the master bedroom. 'Please excuse me a moment,' he said to the Wilsons, and he lit a candle and went upstairs to investigate.

On the second landing he came upon a strange scene. Morgan was down on both knees, peeping through the keyhole of the empty room. On the floor were fragments of putty that the Welshman had removed from the keyhole, and in his left hand he held the penknife that had he used to clear the keyhole. Next to the fragments on the floor was a spent match, which the lodger had used to light his way in the dark at the top of the stairs.

'Morgan! What on earth are you doing, man?' Mr Henshaw asked, but Morgan didn't reply. He was visibly trembling and foaming at the mouth. His right eye, which was pressed against the keyhole, was bulging, and the other eye was still clenched shut. He started to make peculiar animal sounds, like the startled little yelps a man might make when having a nightmare.

'Morgan? What's the matter man? Answer me, will you?'

The landlord touched the Welshman's shoulder, at which he instantly keeled over and seemed to suffer a fit of some sort. Mr Henshaw bounded back down the stairs, dropping the candle at one point, and barged back into the pub's bar in a highly agitated state. He told his wife and the Wilsons that Morgan had collapsed and suffered a fit, and Mr Wilson went to fetch a local doctor he knew at the Sailor's Home. Wilson rode a hansom cab to the Sailor's Home and returned within fifteen minutes. Morgan was still foaming at the mouth on his return, and had become hysterical. His eyes were fixed on the door of the empty room, and he backed away in terror, falling down a flight of stairs and injuring his arm. He was sedated by the doctor and taken to the Infirmary, but the doctors were unable to get a word out of him.

Very shortly afterwards, Peter Morgan became

paralysed for days, and when he finally came out of the paralysis he burst into a paroxysm of maniacal laughter. Experts examined the Welshman but were unable to extract a word of sense out of him, and he ended his days in an asylum for the insane.

For years, Annie Henshaw and others wondered what could possibly have turned the mind of Peter Morgan that night, and Tom Henshaw never mentioned the way he had found Morgan staring through that keyhole. The landlord suspected something evil was at large in the empty room above the pub; something so utterly terrifying that the eyes of no man could behold it without rendering him insane with fear. And Tom Henshaw quickly blocked up the keyhole to the room in question again with putty, and never attempted to open the door to the room again during his tenure at the Old Post Office.

The Dark Side of Aquarius

We often think of the 1960s as a decade of liberated minds and free love, but those who lived through that decade will know that there was also an Occult Renaissance throughout the West in those times, and many believed the long-promised golden Age of Aquarius had finally arrived with the emergence of the Sixties counter-culture. Perhaps the Aquarian Age did begin in that decade, but if that was so there was also another, darker side to Aquarius.

On the wintry Monday afternoon of 3 January 1961, a sinister arsonist struck at four Liverpool churches. At St Charles Roman Catholic Church, Aigburth, at 1.30pm, someone placed a bundle of Bibles in the Christmas crib and set them alight. This person then kindled another fire with destructive consequences at Holy Trinity Church, Wavertree, at around 3pm, and, as in the first act of arson, the diabolical fire-starter was not seen by any witnesses. The flames from the second attack caused severe damage to the staircase, balcony, and vestry. Later that dark afternoon at 5pm, at St Margaret's Church in Anfield, someone once again used Bibles for fuel and the crib as a fireplace. Again, no one saw the firebug enter or leave the church, which only deepened the mystery. Days before, the same arsonist had stacked Bibles in the crib at Walton Parish Church and set them alight, filling the place of worship with choking fumes.

Police naturally suspected that some religious fanatic, or perhaps even a worshipper of Satan, was at large, but someone in authority told the press to back off because they feared there was a 'strange organisation' at work, which was coordinating a spate of arson attacks on churches of every denomination across the country. The Liverpool church fires were just part of a national clandestine campaign waged by a secret society that was literally Hell-bent on eradicating the Christian church.

Special police patrols kept watch on the churches of Liverpool, and detectives looked into the activities of several cults in the city and beyond, including the popular Tiki sect, a cult based on the worship of the Polynesian god, Tiki. This sect would later be investigated by Deputy Chief Constable Herbert Balmer to establish if one of its members had been responsible for the so-called 'ritual' murder of 27-year-old Maureen Ann Dutton at her Knotty Ash home on Thingwall Lane on 20 December of that year.

At the time there was a Satanic cult at large in Liverpool and Wirral, and the members of this strange sect held bonfire Sabbaths at Bowring Park, Prescot, Sefton, Knowsley, Bidston and Thurstaston Common.

One evening, in June 1961, two policemen on the Childwall beat were led to the cemetery of a local church by a group of children who had seen men and women in black hoods and dark green robes, digging up a coffin. The police investigated, and sure enough a grave had been disturbed. One of the policemen then spotted a bearded man in a long white robe standing across the road by the Childwall Abbey Hotel, staring towards the church gates. The police went to talk to the man, and saw he was standing there in his bare feet, but before they reached him, he vanished before their eyes. This incident was witnessed by two policemen, five children, and two passers-by. When the policemen shone a torch into the grave disturbed by the robed occultists, they saw a coffin, minus its lid, and within it lay the very same bearded and barefooted man – lying stretched out in his white burial shroud – who had just performed the vanishing trick outside the Childwall Abbey pub.

Now, around the time of the arson attacks on the city's churches, in January 1961, two regular middle-aged drinkers in the Old Post Office pub, Larry Kilvane and Stuart Swithin, noticed three well-spoken young men (none of them older than 21) who began to frequent the public house at lunchtime on most days. Kilvane and Swithin, both shop-owners who had premises in nearby Ranelagh Street, overheard the three youths talking about the decline in interest in organised religions and young people's growing fascination with the occult. Stuart Swithin was something of a religious man, and he was furious when he heard one of the students say, 'It's time for Christianity to go, it's had its day.' Then the blasphemous trio lifted their glasses in the air and gave a chilling toast. 'Hail to Satan!' the four voices chanted three times.

This was too much for Stuart Swithin and he slammed his pint glass down on the counter of the bar, swivelled on his stool to face the three young men, and walked over to their table. 'Are you students may I ask?'

'Yes, we are, why?' said the bespectacled, red-haired member of the trinity.

Swithin leaned over the red-haired youth and through gritted teeth he said: 'Well, what type of tripe is that you've just been coming out with, if you're supposed to be educated? Toasting the Devil and all that rubbish!'

'It's a free country, haven't you heard? And we can toast who we damn well like,' said the ginger-haired youth, and his two friends giggled.

'You said Christianity's got to go. Why is that?' Swithin asked, and he took out a Woodbine cigarette, lit it and took a long drag.

The answer from the bespectacled student was unexpected, and caught Swithin off his guard: 'Because it's all lies to keep people in check. There's no geographical heaven, is there? Sputnik never hit any of the angels up there, did it? So if the Church lies about things like that, what other rot has it been brainwashing the people with?'

Stuart Swithin threw back his head, blew a cloud of smoke into the air, and came back with his weak reply. 'What the Hell are you talking about? Sputnik and angels? You're off your rocker.'

'People like you are to blame,' said a raven-haired, buck-toothed student, who seemed to be the youngest of the three. 'You just follow the rest of the sheep and never question anything. You're a mindless robot.'

'Oh I'm a mindless robot, am I?' seethed Swithin, and he shook his head and tried to smile off the insult. 'Well you're a wooden-top who toasts the Devil. How barmy is that then, eh?'

'Stu!' Swithin's friend shouted from his barstool, 'Leave them to it, mate. They're just a bunch of daft students. Take no notice; they'll have to live in the real world with the rest of us taxpayers when they leave uni.'

'Yeah, you're right, Larry. Let's see how smarmy the three stooges are when they've got to work for a living!' Swithin said, shooting an expression that lay somewhere between a sneer and a snarl at the three youths before he returned to the bar.

Outside, thunder rolled in the heavy grey skies, heralding a cloudburst of hail which battered the windows of the Old Post Office. An old woman in a mackintosh and headscarf came into the pub, shivering, followed by a woman of about fifty. They were a Mrs Normandy, a blind woman, and her daughter, Enid. Mrs Normandy took off her scarf and shook the hailstones from it as Enid led her to the bar. Stuart and Larry knew the old woman and her daughter well, the two of them being regulars, and Stuart ordered a small shot of Lamb's Navy Rum for Mrs Normandy and a glass of malt stout for Enid.

As Mrs Normandy passed the table where the devil-promoting students were seated, she gave out a loud shriek, and first turned to face the trio, then backed away with a look of shock on her heavily-wrinkled face. She backed into Larry, who spilt a little of his drink in the collision.

'Mum, what's wrong?' Enid asked, and grabbed her mother by the arm before turning to see what had upset

108

her. She saw nothing but the three students sitting silently around the table in the corner, though she noticed the unsettling smiles on their faces. Thunder rumbled outside as the hail shower intensified for about half a minute. Mrs Normandy whispered to her daughter that there was something evil in the corner, but Enid just laughed and said, 'Oh don't be daft, Mum; there're just three lads sitting there, that's all.'

The shower of hail seemed to have ended, and the three students got up and left the pub. It had not escaped Stuart Swithin's notice that Mrs Normandy had sensed something evil in the spot where the three students had been sitting. He thought it odd, but deemed it wise not to say anything about the young men's unsavoury blasphemous views.

A week or so later, Stuart Swithin was sitting behind the counter of his shop, reading the previous day's edition of the *Liverpool Echo*, when he noticed an article about suspected Devil worship taking place in St James's Cemetery. Seven men, and more shocking still in those days, two women, had been seen dressed in black robes performing what was surmised to be a Black Mass in the cemetery. The witnesses were two local residents and an elderly man who had been sitting at his brazier near Gambier Terrace, watching some roadworks. The police had investigated the scene of the suspected Satanic rites and had allegedly found the stone lid of a tomb, which had weighed a quarter of a ton, that had been lifted off a sepulchre to allow access to the mortal remains of a girl.

Swithin lived in a flat on Falkner Street at the time, and decided, rather foolishly, to take a night-time stroll down to St James's Cemetery to see if he could observe any of the Satanists performing their rites. On the first night, Swithin saw nothing except a drunken tramp staggering between the snow-peppered gravestones, but on the second night, he went down to the place of the dead much later, at almost one in the morning, and upon this occasion the shop-owner could hardly believe his eyes as he spied on the eerie proceedings from the darkness of the arched tunnel that forms a sloping entrance to the cemetery.

There was a small bonfire burning about thirty yards from the memorial to William Huskisson, and around it stood six robed figures with pointed hoods, reminiscent of the hoods warn by the Ku Klux Klan in the deep south of America. There was a seventh person present, and as Swithin squinted with watering eyes in the bitter-cold razor-edged wind, he could just discern that the seventh figure was a nude female, and she was standing on one leg in a very unnatural posture before the fire. The girl was obviously double-jointed, because she stood on one leg, and the other leg was bent in such a way that the ball of the foot was touching the back of the girl's head, which was tilted backwards. Her right arm was extended vertically so that her fingers pointed to the sky, and the other arm was rigidly extended so that the fingers of her left hand pointed to the ground.

Swithin felt the urge to get a little nearer to the nocturnal ritual, and he gingerly crept out a few feet from the black mouth of the arched tunnel. The logical hemisphere of Swithin's brain told him to turn around and run, but the curious, childish half of his mind told him to get nearer still to the occultists, and the idea of hiding behind one of the tall gravestones to spy on the figures gave him quite a thrill. Swithin was partly shamed by this feeling of excitement, but he was mesmerised by the lurid flames and titillated by the nude young woman and her surreal posture. He just had to know what arcane practices were about to take place, even at the risk of being caught and possibly killed by these strange people.

The hooded men started to chant something in low voices, and as Swithin crept nearer, he could hear the fire crackling. The naked woman remained as still as a statue, and then, suddenly, the top-most flames of the fire turned a deep indigo colour, and gradually formed a grotesque oval face with black almond shaped eyes, and a crescent-shaped dark mouth. It reminded Swithin of the classic masks representing Comedy and Tragedy that are often depicted on the facades of theatres. The luminous deep-blue face then became purple, and all of the hooded disciples bowed to it and stopped chanting.

At this point, Stuart Swithin lost his nerve when he believed that the ethereal evil-looking entity hovering over the fire had spotted him. Its head turned, presenting its unearthly face directly at the snooper, and its mouth opened and closed, as if it was perhaps informing the hooded men about the uninvited watcher. Swithin was in his fifties, and yet he tried to run like a man half his age. His legs felt sluggish, and before he had even reached the arched tunnel he was fighting for his breath, and his lungs were aching. Behind him he heard a tumult of raised voices, and he knew that the sinister practitioners of the Dark Arts had noticed his clumsy retreat, and would do anything to prevent him from betraying their arcane secrets.

Swithin slipped on a patch of glass-hard ice halfway up the tunnel, and landed on his hands, badly grazing them. He quickly scrambled to his feet as he heard the

111

fast-moving footfalls of his robed pursuers getting ever nearer, and at this point something terrifying occurred which remains inexplicable, even to this day.

As Swithin hurried up the slight incline of the tunnel, he expected to see the arched exit to a street lit by lamp-posts, but instead, there was something standing in the archway near the exit, and at first it looked like the silhouette of some giant snowman with the classic circular body and spherical head, but this snowman had pointed ears and a tail. As Swithin veered to the right to try and avoid the thing, he saw that it was something inexplicable according to the laws of logic of this world. It was a gigantic black cat, well over six feet in height. As it sat there its olivine eyes could only be described as satanic, and they thinned as the great feline beast opened a massive mouth and hissed at Swithin as he flew past into the well-lit street.

He kept on running until, when he was halfway down Rodney Street, he came across the welcoming sight of a policeman on the beat. He told the policeman what he had just witnessed in St James's Cemetery, but did not dare to mention the giant cat, in case he was arrested for being drunk and disorderly. Understandably, the policeman advised Mr Swithin to go home at once and to desist from making a habit of visiting cemeteries after dark in the future.

On the following day at noon, Stuart left an assistant in charge of his shop on Ranelagh Street and called in at the Old Post Office pub. A few minutes after Swithin's arrival, his friend Larry Kilvane entered the pub, and Swithin told him about the uncanny ritual he had witnessed in St James's Cemetery and how he had been chased by six Satan worshippers. He even mentioned the creepy

112

oversized cat that had appeared in the arched tunnel. Larry advised his friend to never go into that cemetery after nightfall again, and said the giant cat had probably just been the shadow of some tomcat. 'Light can play very strange tricks at night, Stu,' Larry informed his friend.'

'Honest to god, it was not a trick of the light, Larry,' Stuart was insisting, when in walked the three students he had had words with a few weeks back, and this time they had been joined by four other people; three men and a young woman. Straight away, Swithin recognised her as that same woman, the one who had stood before the fire in that double-jointed posture, as he had seen in the cemetery. There was no doubt about it; her distinctive profile and hair were identical.

'You alright Stu?' Larry asked, noticing the way his friend was gaping at the young woman, who was about nineteen or twenty. As soon as the six youths and the girl had found a place in the far corner of the parlour, Swithin leaned close to Larry and whispered, 'That's the girl I was telling you about.'

'What girl?' Larry Kilvane seemed confused.

'The one who was standing in that weird way in front of the bonfire,' Swithin explained under his breath.

'Stuart, you're becoming obsessed with this Satan worshipping thing; you need to let it go, mate.' Larry patted his back and asked him what he was having.

'That's got to be them,' Swithin said, without taking his eyes off the group in the corner. The student in glasses with the red hair walked over towards Swithin, then ordered seven drinks from the barmaid. He glanced once at Swithin, smirked, and then looked back at his seated friends.

'I'm going,' Swithin told Larry, 'I don't feel safe in here.'

'Don't be daft, Stu,' Larry told him, 'you're blowing this all out of proportion.'

But Swithin walked out of the Old Post Office and didn't set foot in the pub again for months.

Then, something strange happened in April of that year. Larry Kilvane fell ill with pneumonia and had to be hospitalised. His estranged wife walked into Swithin's shop one afternoon and said he'd have to look after his friend's house because she was going to Wales with her boyfriend for a week. Stuart said he was busy, but Mrs Kilvane just threw the keys to Larry's house on to the counter, then turned around and left. Stuart Swithin was furious, but he visited Larry in hospital and told him not to worry because he'd be looking after his house. Larry was still delirious, and he repeatedly told Stuart not to look in his wardrobe.

Swithin had to visit his friend's house that evening to see if there was any mail that needed to be collected and answered. He also thought it a good idea to leave a light on in the kitchen to give the impression that someone was at home. Curiosity got the better of Stuart Swithin, and he went upstairs to his friend's bedroom – and opened the door to the wardrobe. There was nothing there except jackets and suits hanging up, and an assortment of ties on a rack, but then he noticed the small trunk on the floor of the wardrobe, and he opened it at once.

Inside the trunk there was a long black robe, and a black hood with two eye-holes cut into it. Swithin recoiled in shock at the discovery, and it eventually dawned on him that his own dear friend, Larry Kilvane, must have been the seventh male member of that cult. Why and how had Larry got mixed up with such a sect? Swithin desperately wanted to know, and he intended to

114

put some extremely searching questions to his friend as soon as he was well enough to answer them. Alas, he would never be able to unravel the mystery, because Larry died on the following day from complications of his pneumonia.

THE OXFORD
Oxford Street East

The Oxford Hotel public house, known simply as the Oxford or even 'the Ocky' to most of its regulars, is situated close to the Liverpool University campus on Oxford Street East, at the bottom of the hill which gives its name to the surrounding district – Edge Hill. The Oxford stands alone, the sole survivor of the city council's bulldozers, which swept through my old neighbourhood in the 1960s and 1970s, leaving nothing but desolation. Gone is Coates' chippy, the local launderette, and so many meticulously-kept shops of character and convenience, and in their place are uninspiring stretches of barren 'landscaped' terrain, in other words, poorly-maintained shrubs and bushes set in overgrown grass strewn with litter and the odd prophylactic.

As a fairly regular visitor to the Oxford, which was my local at one point in my younger days, I heard of many strange tales that were said to have taken place within its premises over the years. I had several relatives who served as barmaids in the pub, and they too told me of the ghosts that haunt the Oxford's parlour. Even the field behind the pub has seen its fair share of supernatural goings-on. But let us start at the beginning.

The Oxford dates from the mid-nineteenth century, and in the closing years of that bygone golden age of Victoria's British Empire, we come to the first notable reference to the pub's involvement in a very intriguing paranormal mystery.

The Ghostly Castle

Cases of people disappearing without a trace have been reported since written records began. Nine times out of ten, the missing person has either been murdered, or planned his or her disappearance for dubious reasons, the way the late MP John Stonehouse did in 1975, and Lord Lucan before him. Some leave home because of a domestic upset, like the wife who runs off with her neighbour's husband, or the teenager who goes through the runaway phase. But there is another type of disappearance for which no rational explanations apply at all. Some of these disappearances have local connections.

For example, in January 1882, a twelve-year-old girl named Eliza Carter – who came from Chester, and had lived in Liverpool for some time before her parents moved to London East's End – was taken by someone or something off the streets of West Ham one day. Eliza had just been to visit her sister, and when she failed to return home, the police were informed. Then, that same day, Eliza appeared out of nowhere near her school, and she seemed petrified. Her friends told the ashen-faced girl that her mother and father were frantic looking for her and that she should go home at once, to which Eliza simply said, 'I can't go home; they wouldn't let me.'

Eliza Carter never explained who 'they' were, and then she went missing again. This time, at 11 o'clock that night, the twelve-year-old was seen in the company of a middle-aged woman. After that, Eliza was never seen again, but her dress was later found in the middle of a football pitch with all the buttons cut off, and apparently laid out as if by design.

Eliza Carter's vanishing act was just part of the so-called West Ham disappearances, in which around ten to a dozen people, mostly children, vanished off the streets of West Ham over a number of years. Now, here in Liverpool, in 1901, a couple from Cumberland named Peter and Mary Grave, were running the Oxford pub, having recently taken over the business from a local man named George Norris. The domestic servant at the Oxford was a girl of 21 named Annie Wilson, and she also hailed from Cumberland, and had come down to Liverpool with Mr and Mrs Grave.

In the summer of 1901, Annie was visited by her cousin, a beautiful blonde girl of sixteen named Dandy Phoenix, who came from Southport. Dandy hoped to find employment at the Oxford pub as a barmaid, but being a rather shapely and comely girl who tended to dress in rather garish clothes, Mrs Grave thought she was attracting the wrong type of drinkers to the pub, so she removed Dandy from behind the bar and got her to work in the kitchen upstairs.

One afternoon, in August of that year, a strange out-of-season fog descended on the town. Any sensible person would have chosen to stay indoors in such inclement weather, but Dandy was forced to go out into the fog to shop for the Grave family. She was gone for well over an hour, and Mr and Mrs Grave, and the servant Annie Wilson had started to worry about her. It turned out that she had never arrived at Jolliffe's (the local grocers), and no one in the neighbourhood had seen her. Then one of the drinkers at the Oxford found the girl's basket and her shopping list in an alleyway off Grinfield Street.

The entire clientele of the Oxford public house went looking for the girl, but no one could find a trace of her. That evening, police inspector Martin Churchill visited the Oxford and interviewed the staff and regulars, including an old man named Clegg, who was considered to be very wise. Clegg told the detective that he had noticed an odd-looking man of about fifty, with 'sharpish-looking features' and dressed all in black velvet clothes, and with an odd Dartmouth-green hat, which resembled a kind of pointed trilby with a feather in it. Clegg had noticed that this stranger had been slyly ogling Dandy Phoenix whilst she was on duty behind the bar. He also recalled how, when he went to O'Connors, the local tobacconists, to buy a cigar, he happened to see Dandy in the shop, buying pipe tobacco for Mr Grave, and that same stranger with the feather in his hat had been watching her from a dark corner of the shop.

No one in the area knew anyone who matched the description of the man with the feather in his unusual hat, but then a local umbrella maker named Mary Prow came into the Oxford on the following day and deepened the mystery. What she said caused her to be ridiculed. Mary told Inspector Churchill that she and another woman happened to be walking through 'the atrocious fog' as they made their way up Grinfield Street (which is known locally as 'the brew' - the Scottish name for a hill) on the day of the baffling disappearance. At the top of this hill up which Grinfield Street runs, the two women were astounded to see a castle, which looked dark and very sinister. One minute it was there, and then suddenly it was gone.

Mary Prow and her friend ran up the hill to see if the grand fortification was still there, but there was nothing to be seen there but swirling fog. Mary thought this ghostly vision of the castle somehow had a bearing on the disappearance of Dandy Phoenix. Everyone in the Oxford pub laughed at the woman's bizarre tale, and the umbrella maker stormed out in a huff.

Half an hour later, Dandy Phoenix barged into the Oxford, dishevelled and in a dreadful state. Her hair was a mess, her clothes were torn, and she was missing a shoe and her straw boater. The teenager looked at Peter Grave, the pub manager, with outstretched arms, and struggled to say something, but before she could utter a word her eyes rolled up into her forehead and she collapsed. A brown bottle of smelling salts was promptly put under her delicate nose. The girl recovered her senses, and eventually was able to give a very strange account of her missing time.

Dandy clearly recalled that she had been on her way to Jolliffes the grocers on that foggy afternoon, and she had remembered seeing a man dressed all in black with a strange-looking face, standing in front of her. The man had black piercing eyes, and a pointed long nose. His face looked unreal, as if it was a mask. This stranger smiled at Dandy, and pointed his index finger at her, then curled the finger slowly towards himself, beckoning her towards him. 'Come with me, child,' he said, over and over again in a strange voice, and then, with his left hand, the man pointed to the top of the hill at the end of Grinfield Street, and Dandy saw a castle slowly appear out of the fog. It looked dark and menacing with pointed towers. 'You will be my princess,' said the man. 'Come with me, child.'

Dandy tried to escape down an alleyway, but the man ran after her and dragged her with him. Dandy dropped the basket and shopping list, and suddenly she felt compelled to walk towards the mysterious castle.

At this point, one of the drinkers said, 'Dandy, did the man wear a hat with a feather in, by some chance?'

Dandy's eyes widened and she said, 'Yes, how do you know this?'

'That fiend was seen by someone else,' said the drinker, realising the description of the abductor given by old Mr Clegg had been accurate.

'Come on, Dandy,' said Inspector Churchill, seemingly transfixed by the girl's story, 'tell us what happened next.'

Sniffling, Dandy wiped the tears from her eyes with the back of her little hand, which was bruised – and the girl remembered how she had received that bruise. She said her abductor had gripped her hand so hard that she had cried, and then he had led her through the fog and up the hill, where they both entered the black castle through an arched doorway. From that point on Dandy could remember no more. The next thing the girl knew, she was outside the Oxford pub minus her shoe, with the sensation of the cold pavement on her bare foot.

Inspector Churchill, being a rational hard-boiled soul, couldn't accept Dandy's story, and the Edwardian policeman had certainly never heard of hypnosis, so he couldn't even begin to explain what Dandy had seen in terms of a psychological hypothesis, although he did say that the castle was probably a mirage of St Anne's Church – which happens to look nothing remotely like a castle.

Three years later, in 1904, a group of children, all around the ages of ten to twelve, were playing football on Walker's Playing Fields, off Eaton Road, near Sandfield Park, when they noticed the appearance of something which they would all later unanimously describe as an enormous shimmering castle. Two of the children ran towards this castle but it seemed to move further away from them as they advanced towards it. Then it vanished after about a minute. The mirage, if that is what it was, was described as having pointed towers and spires – which tallies well with the description reported by Dandy Phoenix, Mary Prow, and her friend. Had that mysterious man with the feather in his hat been ready to abduct some children but had been unable to carry out his sinister work for some reason? Who on earth, or off it for that matter, is this mysterious individual, and what is his sinister agenda?

The Witch of Grove Street

In the 1970s, two girls, both aged thirteen, barged into the Oxford public house one night in a distressed state. The barmaid, Maureen, asked them what the matter was, and the girls, Cheryl and Joanne, said they had just met a weird old 'witch' as they came down Florist Street, a lonely lane that leads from the Oxford pub, and lies adjacent to a field bordered by trees and bushes. The girls said the woman chased them and seemed to rise off the ground a few inches and fly after them. A few of the drinkers smirked at the girls' seemingly far-fetched claims, but an old man named Jim said, 'I've seen her many of times over the years,' and the oldster's words soon wiped the inane grins off the faces of the disbelievers, because Jim was known as a very straight-laced and honest man. 'She must be knocking on some years now,' Jim added, 'I'm seventy-six and I first saw her when I was a paper lad ... when I was twelve.'

'A witch?' Maureen the barmaid asked in disbelief. She gave the girls a bottle of lemonade each and asked two of the young lads present to escort the girls back to their homes, which happened to be in a tenement known as Windsor Gardens. Maureen went outside the pub with one of the older drinkers, a man in his sixties, John Kennelly, and they surveyed the field behind the Oxford. At the far end of the field, in the shadows of St Stephen's Church, which was scheduled for demolition, they saw the eerie silhouette of a woman in a skirt that went down to her ankles. Maureen thought she could make out a few details of this woman as she squinted into the darkness. Her hair looked white or grey and was piled up in a bun. The woman had on some sort of apron, and held a basket. Then this woman moved sideways in a strange sliding motion, 'as if she was on castors' Maureen recalls.

The barmaid and the drinker went back into the pub, and Stan went a short distance to his home on Smithdown Lane and fetched a pair of binoculars he used for bird watching. He and Maureen then sneaked out of the side door of the pub again, and peeped around the corner from a vantage point cloaked in shadow The woman was bending down, picking up something in the grass. Stan lifted the binoculars to his eyes and his thumb turned the focus wheel. A hugely-magnified image of the old woman came into view. She was looking directly at Stan, as if she knew he was watching from the shadows. 'Ooh, she looks a weird one, Maureen,' Stan said, and he handed the binoculars to the barmaid. She took a look through them and gasped. 'Oh my God, she knows we're watching her!' said Maureen, and a cold shudder ran down her spine. The woman moved backwards with that eerie unnaturally-rapid sliding motion into the shade of the trees.

Years later, in 1980, a female figure which seems to have been the same woman sighted on the previous occasions, was seen again in the field behind the Oxford pub when a girl in her early twenties named Susan spotted her as she walked down Oxford Street East. Susan noticed the silhouetted figure of a woman in a long dress carrying a basket in the field that lies between Florist Street and Grove Street. As she neared the Oxford pub, the silhouette literally hovered across the grass towards the young woman, and Susan let out a scream and ran straight into the pub, where she cause quite a stir amongst the drinkers with her dramatic entrance. Susan was so frightened, she was unable to tell the regulars what had happened to her outside, and she looked at the door of the bar room in terror, as if she expected the figure to come through it at any minute.

'What is it, Sue?' asked the barmaid, full of concern. 'What's up, pet?'

Susan thought the barmaid and the drinkers would only laugh at her, so she said nothing and pretended a stray dog had chased her. But then afterwards, she decided to confide in a friend about what she'd really been running from, after overhearing a man in the parlour mentioning 'a weird old woman' he had just seen in the field behind the pub, dressed in old-fashioned clothes. The man said this quaint old lady had been stooping down, and seemed to be picking some plants out of the grass and putting them into her basket. The man had glanced at his watch, and looked back towards the old woman and she had vanished.

On the following day, Susan went to the spot in the field behind the Oxford pub to see what type of plants the creepy woman had been picking, and came upon a large cluster of toadstools.

The reports of the old woman with the basket petered out around the end of the 1990s, but she may still make the occasional appearance in that field behind the Oxford public house. Her identity is unknown, but if she's the same person who was seen back in the seventies, she must be remarkably old, or she may in fact be a spirit – or perhaps a witch, and this latter possibility leads us rather appropriately to the following incident, which concerns the so-called Witch of Grove Street.

Where Are You, My Love?

As child I lived on Melville Place, off Oxford Street, and heard many strange tales about the neighbourhood from my grandmother and her friends, who were all surviving Victorians. One of the earliest stories I recall concerned a man named Leigh Maddocks (or possibly Maddox) who lived in the Bootle area in Edwardian times.

In the winter of 1905, Mr Maddocks came to stay at a lodging house on Oxford Street East, close to the Oxford pub, which he soon began to frequent. The Bootle man seemed to be an educated, well-heeled fellow, and was perhaps a clerk or academic, but those who drank with him learned a little of his sad background when the whiskey loosened his tongue. Maddocks had been deserted by his lover, Mary Morris, who was considerably younger than him, and he had heard that she had settled somewhere in the vicinity of the pub, hence, he had taken up lodgings locally, hoping to find Mary. It was Maddocks' custom to always take out a locket from his inside jacket pocket, open it, and look at the vignette photograph of Mary before leaving the pub, just before final orders was called. Some of the curious at the Oxford would then watch the pathetic broken-hearted man walk the streets, perhaps because he had become plagued by insomnia after the loss of his love, or maybe because he hoped he would somehow eventually find Miss Morrison.

On one such night, close to the hour of 1am, Leigh Maddocks was mournfully walking up the lonely dark lane known as Florist Street, next to the Oxford pub, when a thick sodden slate-grey sea mist began to infiltrate the area, rolling across pavements and snaking down alleyways. He was suddenly aware of an aged female voice calling something out to him. Maddocks halted, nervously, and on turning round jumped when he noticed the silhouette of an old hunchbacked woman at the entrance of a nearby alleyway. Her words became clearer and she told him she knew who he was seeking and claimed she had the means to find her. This immediately caught the attention of the love-sick Maddocks, and he eagerly followed the old woman as she led him through the alleyway and out on to a foggy Grove Street.

Here, by the ghostly diffused light of an incandescent mantle glowing at the top of a nearby lamp-post, he could make out for the first time the grotesque features of the old crone, and although he found her face utterly repugnant, almost reptilian, he kept on following her because of the apparent promise she held of finding his beloved Mary. The old woman led him under an archway into an alleyway that was so black, he constantly stumbled and tripped on the cobbles as he blindly placed one foot in front of another.

At last he heard a door open, and crossed a yard leading to some steps which led down into a cellar, which apparently belonged to the old hag. Once inside she lit an oil-lamp to reveal a midden of dust-coated jars, bottles, cans, a rusty old mangle, and a fireplace filled with a mound of ash in which a few dying embers faintly glowed.

The woman said she would give Maddocks two small bottles of ointment that would make his eyes and ears so acute, he would surely see and hear his lost love, because they would transform his senses so that he had the sharpness of a cat. Ten pounds was the asking price, and Maddocks paid her there and then without hesitation, for although outwardly the woman was a wrinkled abomination, he sensed that she sincerely sympathised with his troubles, as if she too had once lost a love and knew what he was going through. He thanked her profusely once the purchase had been made and the instructions on how to use the ointments had been given. Then, halting by the cellar door, as the night vapours swirled about him, Mr Maddocks asked, 'What is your name?'

'Reaky,' she replied, and then smiling, looked down at the floor, where she picked up a mouse. She stroked it in her palm, and added, 'Agnes Reaky.'

Leigh Maddocks rushed straight home to his lodgings and immediately applied the strange ointments. Firstly, he applied the green-tinted oily lotion to his right eye, to test its effects, and about half a minute after doing so, his conjunctiva became greatly inflamed. Loudly, he cursed the old woman, thinking she had cruelly tricked him by selling him some worthless pepper-laced concoction, and the landlady banged on the wall and told him to be quiet. After Maddocks had bathed his inflamed eye in water, he glanced out beyond the panes of his window and was surprised to find that the neighbourhood had taken on a purplish tint. He could see a policeman walking in the thick fog on the pavement below – but only with his right eye, the one into which he had rubbed the ointment! When he covered his right eye and looked at the same scene with his left eye, he could see only dense fog; the pavement was totally obscured.

The old woman's claims for her strange ointment had been true after all, and so Maddocks quickly applied the green teal ointment to his left eye, and after the burning sensation in the eye socket had subsided, he bathed it and looked again out of the window to find that he could see Oxford Street as if it were daytime. Even more amazing, when he squinted at the policeman on his beat, he could almost make out the constable's number on his collar – as if his eyes now had the ability to zoom in on objects like the eyes of an eagle.

Maddocks chuckled to himself, and then he

remembered the other ointment which Agnes Reaky had given him to boost his hearing. He uncorked the tiny bottle and tapped out a runny yellow liquid on to his palm. He dipped the smallest finger of his hand into the ointment and inserted the coated digit into his right ear. Then he did the same with his other ear. About a minute later, the sounds of veritable waterfall – a Niagara Falls of ambient sound – roared in Maddocks' ears, and at first he found it unbearable, and he placed his palms over his ears and threw himself down on the bed. Then came explosive knocks on the walls like cannon fire; it was the landlady thumping on her wall, which adjoined his. A voice, which must have sounded like the roar of a Tyrannosaurus Rex, blasted the sensitised ears of Mr Maddocks, and then came the rhythmic bass drum of his own heart in his ears. Even his intake of breath sounded loud and sharp, but then the amplification subsided slightly, to a more bearable level.

Maddocks quickly put on his hat, coat and scarf, and left the lodging house as quietly as he could to roam the night-time streets on his usual mission, but this time equipped with his hyper acute sight and hearing. He prowled the fogbound streets of Liverpool like a cat – eyes and ears twitching at every tiny sound or movement. He lingered in the alleyways of Upper Canning Street and listened to the infra-sounds of conversations taking place high above him in the eaves and bedrooms of the grand houses; servants gossiping in hushed tones about their employers, and solemn promises being whispered between lovers in their beds.

By dawn, the effects of the ointment had worn off, leaving Maddocks feeling almost blind and deaf by comparison. Later that day he called in at the Oxford public house for company, and the landlord, who was at that time a man named Morgan Taylor, was telling a handful of drinkers that a burglar had been on the prowl last night. The publican said he had been unable to sleep because of a rheumatic complaint, and had been sitting at his bedroom window around 3am, watching the fog blanket the area as he smoked his pipe, when he had noticed a man in a wide felt hat, 'Just like the one you wear, Mr Maddocks,' he said, pointing to Maddocks' head. 'So make sure you all lock up well tonight,' Taylor told the drinkers, adding that he had a 'nice surprise' waiting for the burglar, should he happen to see him lurking about again.

'Oh aye, and what would that be, Morgan?' asked one of the regulars, and the landlord left the parlour with a childish smile, went upstairs, and returned a minute later with a ridiculous-looking blunderbuss in one hand and an old Claymore sword in the other. 'Let any robber in all of rascaldom face these two,' Taylor said, holding the archaic Scottish sword aloft, and he then launched into his well-known anecdotes of his alleged exploits in the Second Afghan war.

Maddocks sneaked out of the pub and decided to roam another part of the district that night, in case the insomniacal landlord spotted him and carried out his threat. Night soon arrived, and Leigh Maddocks applied the witch-ointments and left the lodging house via the backyard door. On this night a fog failed to materialise, and a waning moon shone on the glistening iced rooftops of the city. All was as still as the grave, and the only sound was the gentle pad of Maddocks' feet as he walked up Grove Street towards Toxteth. 'Where are you, my love?' he whispered to himself, but even soliloquising under his breath sounded like a town crier, so he walked along, heading south towards Mulgrave Street, his sharpened eyes scanning everything, and his ultrasensitive ears picking up minute whisperings that no man would normally be able to hear: a starving stray dog barking half a mile distant, somewhere on Lesseps Road; the gentle jangling of a bell on a buoy far out on the Mersey; and now, a very curious thing that excited Maddocks so much, he stopped in his tracks. He could hear a piano playing far away, and an all too familiar voice singing along with it – Mary Morris! Without a doubt, it was his darling Mary's voice, and the song she was singing was one of her favourites – 'Wont You Buy My Pretty Flowers?' by Messrs French and Persley.

Maddocks swivelled his head right and left, trying to get a bearing on the origin of the wonderful singing voice. He turned around and realised it was coming from the direction of Falkner Square, from one of those grand Georgian stucco wedding cake white houses yonder. He started to walk back up Mulgrave Street and then turned left into the square. His heart pounded in his ears now because he could see silhouettes moving behind the saffron curtains. He walked up to the gate of the house and looked up at the drawing room window. His heart fell. The woman's shadow looked a bit too curvaceous and corpulent to be tat of Mary Morris. 'Sir,' came a sudden voice floating on the night air. Maddocks jumped, startled. He had been so convinced that Mary was the singer, he hadn't noticed the heavy footsteps of the policeman plodding up behind him on his midnight beat. 'Why are you loitering here, Sir?' the policeman asked, then, without waiting for a reply, firmly advised Maddocks to 'Move along, go on, off you go.'

'Oh, good evening, officer,' was Maddocks' response, and he smiled and explained, 'I was just listening to that woman singing. It's beautiful, isn't it?'

'What woman?' the policeman asked, his eyebrows dipped with puzzlement.

'Why that woman,' said Maddocks and he nodded towards the great white house in the corner of the square, but now the saffron curtains had faded to become a taupe grey. Not a single light shone from that building.

There was a frozen pause. The policeman's thin mouth almost elongated into a smile under his thick handle-bar moustache, and in a somewhat reticent voice, he said, 'That's the haunted house. Didn't you know? You say you could hear her singing?' Maddocks nodded twice. 'I haven't heard her myself, but a lot have. She died a few years ago. Suicide … terrible business.' The policeman shook his head and pursed his lips. 'She was jilted, you see. She put her head on a railway line. Horrible it was … gruesome … and so young too.'

'I don't think it was a ghost, officer. She looked much too real and alive for that,' Maddocks said with an uneasy lopsided smile.

'Well I look real as well, don't I?' the policeman asked, thinning his eyes with a serious look. 'And I'm one aren't I?'

Maddocks was confused for a moment and then he noticed two things. There was no cloud of exhaled breath coming from the policeman's mouth, despite the freezing weather, and below his knees he was partially transparent. Maddocks backed away in shock.

'Why are you living so afraid of us? We were like you lot once you know?' said the ghostly policeman, walking towards Maddocks.

Just then a light flared up again in the window of the house in the corner of the square, and once more the ethereal piano began to play 'Won't You Buy My Lovely Flowers?' This time it had an altogether different effect on poor Maddocks, who turned away and ran as fast as his legs could carry him. The deceased policeman let out a belly laugh as he watched him flee.

All the way back to the lodging house, Maddocks was prey to every ghost, phantom and demon that was at large under the moon that night, and even after he had barricaded himself into his room, he kept on hearing unearthly voices, some of them the sobbing cries of children, calling for their mothers. One particular voice – that of an old Irish woman, continued to torment Maddocks as he tried to sleep with a pillow wrapped around his ears. She was screaming vile profanities at Maddocks until finally letting out a bloodcurdling screech when the first beams of the rising sun shone into the room in the morning.

Maddocks obtained a Bible from a fellow lodger and carried it with him when he went in search of Agnes Reaky's cellar hovel, but try as he may, Maddocks never managed to locate her abode. He threw away the ointment which had opened his eyes and ears to a spirit world that should have remained out of bounds to mortals, and that evening, when Maddocks told landlord Taylor about Mrs Reaky, the publican warned him to have no further dealings with the so-called Witch of Grove Street. 'She preys on people's problems and predicaments, that one, and she's been seen skulking about outside of here, eavesdropping, and fishing for victims such as yourself,' Taylor told Maddocks, and as he finished speaking, the eerie shadow of the hunchbacked hag flitted past the window of the pub.

Alfred Blackshaw, an elderly drinker, bent his ear to Maddocks' story about the loss of his sweetheart, and advised him to let it be, and to return home. 'If that lass still harbours any affection for ye, then she'll surely come back to ye,' he said. Maddocks reluctantly took his advice, and returned to Bootle on the very next day, resigned but broken.

In the spring of that year, Leigh Maddocks walked into the Oxford, this time with Mary Morris on his arm. Maddocks had come to tell the landlord and the wise old man Blackshaw about his engagement and they all drank a toast to the reunited couple. They say the landlord and many of the drinkers at the Oxford pub subsequently attended the wedding of Maddocks and his beloved Mary.

THE CAMBRIDGE
Cambridge Street

The Scratch on the Cheek

One sunny pleasant afternoon in July 1975, a Jewish businessman named Ben sat smoking a cigar in a corner of the Cambridge public house, which is situated on the corner of Mulberry Street and Cambridge Street, on the campus of Liverpool University. Each weekday at lunchtime, Ben liked to walk from his textile warehouse off London Road to the Cambridge, a pub he had frequented back in the days when he had been at university, and on this day, he was sipping a gin and tonic between long satisfying puffs on his cigar, mentally extrapolating his profits and musing on his proposed expansion into other premises, which he'd had his eye on in the city centre, when he felt a brief sharp pain on his left cheek. He touched the site of the pain with his index finger and saw he was bleeding.

He took a cotton handkerchief from the top pocket of his jacket and dabbed at his cheek, then went to the pub toilet to inspect the cut in the mirror. There was a thin red line, about two centimetres long, an inch below his left eye. Baffled as to the cause of the cut, he then dabbed it again and it soon stopped bleeding. He returned to his corner seat, where he finished his cigar, then left the pub at around 1.15pm and returned to his warehouse.

Just under a week later, Ben visited the Cambridge again and this time he bumped into an old university pal named Trevor, who happened to be paying a visit to the pub out of search for nostalgia. Trevor had also done very well for himself since graduating, and was now a stockbroker living in Cheshire and he had driven from his home near Frodsham on his day off just to take a stroll down memory lane to the old haunts of his student days.

Trevor joined Ben in his favourite corner of the pub, and the two were soon mulling over old times and laughing at the antics they had got up to as students. What would their colleagues and employees think if they knew? But Ben suddenly stopped laughing when he noticed the same bizarre injury he himself had sustained just six days before appearing on Trevor's left cheek. Trevor instantly flinched with pain and felt for the thin gash which had appeared from nowhere on his face. He thought he must have been stung at first, but then Ben told his startled friend how the same thing had recently happened to him, and Trevor, who, unlike the secular down-to-earth Ben, was a believer in the supernatural, cried, 'Oh my god!' and then sheepishly suggested that the thing which had cut him might have been a ghost.

A woman who worked as a secretary at Senate House, just around the corner on Abercromby Square, was sitting at the next table enjoying a liquid lunch-break. Having overheard the conversation and having seen the gash on Trevor's face, she gave a knowing glance at him and said, 'It did that to me once.' Trevor asked what 'it' was, and the woman said: 'They reckon it's the ghost of a woman. I don't know who she was or why she does it, but about two years ago I was sitting there, exactly where you are and the same thing happened to me for no apparent reason. It was like a long thin paper cut, but quite deep and very painful. I believe it's happened to a few people.'

Of course, this served to confirm Trevor's suspicions and he emailed me to see if I might know which ghost was responsible for inflicting what appeared to be deep straight scratches on people's faces, but I had to admit complete bafflement. I mentioned the phenomenon on the radio in the hope that a member of the public could throw some light upon the metaphysical matter and I received quite a few first-hand accounts that seemed to back up the reports from Ben and Trevor, but they still failed to identify the sadistic entity.

Dave and Abigail Latham got in touch with me at the studios of Radio Merseyside after I had mentioned the cheek-scratching spook, and said that just before Christmas, 1967, when they had been teenaged students, they had both sustained the exact same cuts to their faces as I had described in my broadcast. Abigail had even recorded the weird incident in a diary she had kept at the time. On this occasion, they heard what they described as a 'harsh whispering' sound by their table. It sounded like the gravelly subdued voice of an old woman. Abigail yelped as she felt something cold slice into the left cheek of her face, and a few seconds later, as Dave leaned forward to look at his girlfriend's wound, he too was cut.

A woman who worked at the Cambridge pub as a barmaid in the 1970s also got in touch to tell me how, one evening, after the pub had closed, she was collecting glasses when she felt something brush past her – in the corner where most of the cheek-cutting incidents have taken place. The barmaid thought that maybe she had imagined the encounter with something, because she admitted to being overtired, but then suddenly there was a loud bang, and two half-pint glasses on the counter of the bar shattered into tiny fragments.

Portent Outside a Pub

Being raised on Myrtle Street, which is in close proximity to the Cambridge pub, I heard the following strange story about the drinking establishment many years ago from a late uncle.

In the spring of 1913, four young men, all friends who lived and worked in Edge Hill, were drinking in the Cambridge pub one weekend afternoon, when one of them thought he heard a rumbling sound outside. His friends told him it was probably distant thunder (even though the skies were blue outside), but then everyone present also heard a faint whistling sound coming from outside. Leaving their pints on the table, the four men ran out of the pub via the Cambridge Street door and listened intently to a succession of distant thuds and explosive sounds – and the racket seemed to be coming from the sky. Then came a faint whistling sound, which suddenly started to fall in pitch as it grew louder and louder – as if something was falling towards the pub out of the sky.

The four men froze, alarmed by this unusual phenomenon, and a ferocious bang – equivalent to the detonation of a hundred firecrackers – sent the lads running for cover inside the pub. The odd thing was that the other drinkers in the pub had heard nothing. They were still sitting over their pints, some chatting, some idly staring into space, when the four men went back inside.

The strange incident was soon forgotten, and in the following year, those four men volunteered to fight for their country after the outbreak of the First World War. Before long, like all the other eager young recruits, they found themselves listening, on the battlefields of France, to the same terrible roaring sounds they had heard that spring day outside the Cambridge pub, as the might of the German artillery bombarded the four lads and their compatriots in the trenches. Three of those lads were killed by a whistling shell that all four heard as it arced towards them – and the lone survivor was left deafened and shell-shocked for months afterwards. When he eventually came home, he stood for a long while in the doorway of the Cambridge pub, the place where he and his four deceased mates had somehow been confronted by a portent of death.

The Subterranean Scotsman

The Cambridge pub was originally known as the Spirit Vaults in the late 1840s, and was always a popular watering hole for the locals.

In May 1884, Harry Hammond, a colourful landlord of the pub, handed ownership of the Cambridge over to Edward Jones. The new manager was something of a gambler, who allowed all-night poker games to go on at the pub after it had closed to the public.

Just before Christmas 1886, Jones was in the middle of a game of poker with seven other gamblers in the Cambridge when play was interrupted by the faint strains of what sounded like bagpipes. Jones cautiously pulled the curtains aside a few inches and looked out on to a snowy Mulberry Street. There wasn't a soul about, just some poor stray mongrel dog trotting languidly past. Jones went to the other window, and gently moved the heavy drapes an inch apart to look out on to Cambridge Street, but again, all he could see was a deserted snow-covered street.

The bagpipe music faded, but at about three in the morning it returned, and most of the gamblers agreed that the eerie music was coming from somewhere beneath them. Imagining some crazy Scotsman was in the pub's cellar, Eddy Jones enlisted the help of a couple of the gamblers to go down to the cellar with him, as his wife stood guard over the till and bottles of ale and spirits.

To all intents and purposes the cellar was empty, yet down there the bagpipe music sounded louder. The gamblers and Jones ascertained that the music seemed to be passing underneath the pub on a north-south axis, as if the bagpiper was walking up and down a tunnel running under Mulberry Street.

On hearing this, one of the older gamblers, a Mr Hignett, said there were tunnels running under many parts of the neighbourhood. They had all been excavated by the so-called Mole of Edge Hill, Joe Williamson, but another gambler, a local man named Kinread, argued that Williamson was long dead and buried and anyway, none of his tunnels ran anywhere near the Cambridge.

Eddy Jones was rather superstitious, and was wondering to himself if the bagpipe-player below might be Old Nick himself. Old Mr Hignett read the landlord's fearful expression. 'You're thinking the same as me, aren't you, Eddy?' Hignett asked. 'We might be dealing with the Devil here?'

'What are you talking about now, you old fool?' snapped Jones, with an unconvincing show of bravado.

'Oh Jemima!' cried one of the impatient gamblers, 'Are you two going to argue all night or play this game?'

Before anyone could answer, there came a deafening series of thuds from below, which shook the public house to its foundations.

All of the gamblers leapt to their feet, ready to abandon the pub at once, because each thought the roof was about to cave in. Curtains were tossed back, even at the risk of alerting a patrolling policeman to the illegal poker game. Now the snow was falling so heavily it was barely possible to see the other side of the road. The gamblers could neither see nor explain what had caused the loud thuds, which stopped as abruptly as they had started. Mr Jones, worried that the night's happenings might put his customers off in the future, put more wood on the fire and they all soon settled down to the game again when the whiskey began to flow.

At around four in the morning, as the card-players were beginning to flag, the strains of bagpipes coming from below ground could plainly be heard again, and the Gaelic music soon became so loud, that Jones and the seven gamblers were forced to hold their hands over their ears – and then three mysterious loud earth-shaking thuds rocked the public house. The music stopped. Old Mr Hignett stood up, and addressing the floor, shouted, 'Who is it you want?' Seven pairs of frightened eyes looked at the old man. 'Is it me you've come for?' Hignett asked, as he placed a trembling hand on the back of his chair to steady himself. A strange, unusually heavy silence descended on the place, and even the crackling sounds of the wood burning in the grate seemed muted.

'Have you come for Mr Jones then?' Hignett asked, still speaking to the floor, and the landlord was heard to gulp as he waited for a reply, but none came.

'Is it Mr Kinread here? Is it he you've come for?' Hignett asked, and gave a sidelong glance at Kinread, who was visibly perspiring.

'Then how about Mr MacDonald?' Hignett asked, upon which the floor shook violently three times.

Jim MacDonald, a Dumfries man of thirty-five, slowly rose from his seat with a look of utter terror in his eyes. He made a dash for the door, slid the bolts, and ran out into the snowstorm. Mr Jones and the six other poker players went to the doorway and watched the spooked Scotsman as he was swallowed up by the blinding blizzard. They wondered what he could have done to be so fearful of the sinister entity below.

They found MacDonald dead, from exposure, lying half buried in a snowdrift on the following morning. His bulging terror-stricken eyes looked as if he had been scared to death by something. Some said that MacDonald had stolen from the poor-box of a local church to finance his poker games, whilst others speculated that he had committed a much worse crime, and the Devil had come to claim him as a result.

THE VINES
Lime Street

The Pink Lady

In the summer of 1960, the flamboyant performer Liberace took a touring version of his London Palladium show around the country, and in July 1960, he came to the Liverpool Empire. After the sell-out show, Liberace and his clan of musicians, managers and minders, went to the Vines public house, situated on the corner of Lime Street and Copperas Hill. The jazz musician Johnny Dankworth and his wife Cleo Laine were also at the pub – known locally as the Big House – that evening, and as can be imagined, Liberace and his cortege, caused quite a stir in the parlour with the locals. Scousers are universally known for their sarcastic wit, but fortunately for Liberace that evening, most of the regulars in the Vines found the glitzy showman likeable, and the usual autograph-seekers and star-struck drinkers congregated around the American performer.

Whilst all of this idolisation of Liberace was going on, a strange old woman sat in the far corner of the parlour, with an old fashioned hooded pram tucked in beside her. The woman wore a quaint carnation-pink Edwardian dress, and partially covering her heavily wrinkled face she wore a rose-pink veil, similar in style to the type of veil worn by a bride. Liberace couldn't help but notice her, and discreetly asked the barman who she was. 'The Pink Lady,' said a regular, butting in before the barman could answer.

The barman explained to Liberace and his friends that the old woman was quite an eccentric, who made a living reading people's fortunes with her cards. Just then an elderly man stepped forward and warned the world-famous pianist that he should have nothing to do with the Pink Lady as her predictions always tended to concentrate on the bad things that were about to happen in a person's life, and she was rarely wrong in her interpretation of the cards.

Liberace had a lifelong fascination with the supernatural, and confessed that he couldn't resist fortune-tellers. He himself was actually born with a veil, known as a caul, over his face. A caul is a flap of thin diaphanous skin. Tradition decrees that babies born with such a veil of translucent skin are destined to have psychic gifts.

Liberace enquired as to why the Pink Lady had an old pram by her table, and a few of the regulars told him that no one was really sure, but some thought the old woman had lost a young child in tragic circumstances many years ago and could not accept that he was dead, for she always talked to the pram as if she was addressing a little boy. Liberace felt a little sympathy for the woman, and inquired what her usual tipple was. 'Gin,' said the barman, and so Liberace had a large gin sent over to her.

Half an hour elapsed, before a curious Liberace could resist the lure of the eccentric woman no more, and he walked over to where she was sitting at her table. He introduced himself, and the Pink Lady's smile was just visible behind her veil. 'I hear you read cards,' Liberace began, and he beamed his bright trademark smile at the old woman. She nodded, and in a well-spoken accent she said, 'Yes, I do. Would you like me to read your cards?'

'Yes, I would,' said Liberace, and as people gathered around the table, he added, 'but please be kind, I've had my fair share of bad news in recent years.'

'I can only tell you the truth,' said the Pink Lady, and she produced a quaint-looking dark wooden box from inside the pram. She opened this box to reveal some old playing cards backed with velvet of Tyrian purple. The aged cartomancer uttered a stream of unintelligible words under her breath as she held the deck of cards in her left hand, and then she began to deal them on to the table in a particular pattern.

The three of diamonds was the first card to be turned over. 'A secret wish has come true,' said the old woman, and an engrossed Liberace nodded thoughtfully. The eight of spades was the next card to be revealed, and according to the veiled fortune-teller, that card represented a jealous rival. 'Be careful, son,' she warned. 'Someone is out to take your crown.'

145

A handful of those present laughed, for they already knew of many up-and-coming stars such as Elvis, who had easily overtaken Liberace in the popularity stakes. The seven of diamonds came up, and the Pink Lady said that card was a warning for Liberace not to spread gossip – 'or it shall come back upon you and be very hurtful,' she rasped. The next card to be turned over was the Joker, a throwback to the Fool from the Tarot pack. The old woman said: 'The Joker symbolises a person who has overthrown conventional attitudes, but he is self-indulgent and mischievous.

'Oh, that's me to a tee!' grinned Liberace, and everyone burst out laughing.

This cartomancy session continued for about ten minutes, and Liberace was utterly captivated, because he felt that the old woman's interpretation of the cards offered a great insight into his life: how things stood for him at the moment and where he was going in the future. But he yearned to know more and pressed the Pink Lady for even more revelations. Reluctantly she told him there was a layout of cards which could even predict when the subject would die, but she hardly ever used it because, no matter what the projection, it obviously played on the person's mind. The customer who had warned Liberace against having his cards read by the old crank shot a sombre knowing look at the performer, and shook his head. 'Curiosity killed the cat,' he said to Liberace, and several people present also tried to warn him against dabbling in the darker side of the cards.

'If you did reveal the supposed date when I am supposed to die, could I avoid it somehow?' Liberace asked, consumed with fear and curiosity in equal measure.

The Pink Lady slowly shook her head, and said,

'What will be will be.'

'I think that's enough now, madam,' the barman said to the old woman.

Liberace's manager didn't like the way things were going and added, 'Yes, come on now, Lee (the name by which the pianist was known to his closest friends), let's go.'

But Liberace couldn't restrain himself: 'No, leave this lady alone, I'd like to know. It doesn't necessarily mean any of it will come true, but I'm curious.'

And so the Pink Lady dealt four more cards and lined them up in a single row. The first card was the ace of spades; the next the nine of diamonds – a sinister card that has for generations been known as the 'Curse of Scotland', although nobody knows why. The Pink Lady looked up at Liberace and asked him if the number the cards had dictated so far – 19 – meant anything to him. Liberace was a rather vain man who didn't want people to know his real age, and he may have known that what the woman was driving at was for him to admit that 1919 was the year he had been born – but he just shrugged and said that he could think of no connection. But it was the next two cards that were infinitely more important, because these would surely reveal the year of his death. If those cards were six and one, the gifted pianist was sure that he would probably pass out.

The third card turned out to be an eight of diamonds (which signified a great change, according to the old woman). Everyone was silent and tense as the final card was revealed – the most mystic number of all, according to the occultists: the number seven. The seven seas; the seven Days of Creation in the Bible (which features the number seven quite a lot, including the seven last words of Christ on the cross); seven years' of bad luck if you break a mirror and so on. In this case it was the seven of spades. 'That card signifies a change for the worse,' said the old woman flatly.

'Nineteen-eighty-seven?' Liberace said, deep in thought as he studied the old fashioned cards with a faraway look. A smile slowly spread across his face as he did the simple mental arithmetic. 'Twenty-seven years to go,' he mused, then he whispered something into the ear of a friend, and that person handed the old woman a rolled up bundle of pound notes.

The story of this prediction has been passed on to me from many people who were either there in the Vines pub that evening, or from people who had heard of the story second-hand, so make of it what you will. Wladziu Valentino Liberace, to give him his full name, did indeed die, aged sixty-seven, on 4 February 1987, after suffering a cardiac arrest.

The last report I have of the Pink Lady of the Vines is from 1964, when she supposedly predicted the assassination of a future monarch of Britain, but when this was supposed to take place is not known. Who the Pink Lady was and where she lived is not known, but some people have told me she came from the Toxteth area.

THE BELVEDERE
Sugnall Street

Hello Grandma

You will find the Belvedere pub located in Sugnall Street, a sleepy cul-de-sac in the Georgian Quarter of Liverpool. Here we find a grade II-listed drinking establishment which has provided the backdrop for some intriguing – and terrifying – supernatural phenomena, and I will deal with them in reverse chronological order.

In the early 1980s, Jo a middle-aged Kensington woman, went to visit her heavily-pregnant twenty-one-year-old daughter Hannah at Oxford Street Maternity Hospital one dismal March afternoon. Hannah was due to give birth in just over a week, and her mother, and younger sister Debbie brought her fruits, sweets, and a few magazines to help her while away the long boring hours of waiting. At this time, predicting the sex of a baby was unheard of, yet Jo was convinced the baby would be a boy, because she thought Hannah's swollen abdomen seemed unnaturally wide – and Jo believed in the old superstition which said that the shape of the mother's 'bump' gave an indication of the baby's sex; a wide bump was a boy and a long, narrower bump signified a girl. Hannah was of a different opinion and said she thought she was having a girl. She had even chosen a name for the baby: Kimberly.

After the visit Jo had decided she would go to the Belvedere pub on Sugnall Street, just off Myrtle Street, in the hope of bumping into an old friend named Mona, who lived on nearby Falkner Street. Mona was of Romany descent and was skilled at reading tealeaves and palms. She could even read the patterns left by the froth on a glass of beer.

And so, Jo and her eighteen-year-old daughter Debbie left the maternity hospital and went down Mulberry Street, then turned into Myrtle Street and crossed over by the old Ear, Nose and Throat Hospital. They went into the Belvedere, but there was no sign of Mona. Jo ordered half a pint of lager and lime for Debbie and a gin and tonic for herself. Afterwards, Jo intended to catch the bus on Myrtle Street which would take her and her daughter to Smithdown Road, to call in at a relative's house before getting another bus back to Kensington. Jo lit a cigarette and relaxed in her seat at a table. She took a long drag on her Player's Number 6 and then threw her head back and gently blew a circle of blue smoke up at the high ornate ceiling. The wreaths of smoke were

150

twisting and curling as they spread out and dissipated – when suddenly, Debbie tapped her mother's forearm and cried, 'Mum! Look at that!'

The teenager was staring up at the ceiling near a window that looked out on to Sugnall Street. From the window, a strange swirling ball of smoke was moving slowly towards the mother and daughter. It was about five or six inches from the ceiling, and as it drifted through the air, it seemed to become cloudier. There were only two other people in the parlour – an elderly man in a flat cap who was gazing morosely at the counter, waiting to be served, and a decorator in his painting overalls, sitting in the corner as he read the *Daily Mirror*. Both men were oblivious to the thing moving across the ceiling. The barmaid was turned towards the shelves of bottles, perhaps checking the stock, and so only Debbie and her mother were able to witness the eerie materialisation – which before long had solidified into a tiny baby.

'Holy Mary, Mother of God!' Jo exclaimed.

The ghostly baby was curled up into the classical foetal position: head forward between the knees, and with its arms embracing the lower legs. This baby was like no other they had ever seen, in that it had a head of flowing long red hair, but what really struck Jo and Debbie as weird was the baby's sinister grin.

Then the decorator also noticed the ectoplasmic infant. His big shocked eyes gazed at it over the top of the tabloid. He dropped the newspaper to his lap, swore under his breath, and exclaimed, 'What the hell is that?'

'Oh, Mum!' yelped Debbie, 'What d'you think it is?' And she went to get up, with a view to running out of the pub, but her mother's hand seized her arm and Jo said, 'Jesus Christ!' The barmaid turned around at this point and the ghostly baby seemed to fade away before she could see it.

At this point, Jo's old friend Mona came into the pub. 'Well, hello there,' Mona said to Jo, but her friend said nothing in reply; she and Debbie were still looking at the space in mid-air where the spectral baby had been floating. Jo told her friend what she and her daughter – and the decorator – had just seen, and straight away, Mona asked Jo if she knew anyone who was expecting a child, or who had recently given birth to a baby. With a look of absolute dread, Jo looked across at her daughter's face, and Debbie was staring back at her mother with all the colour drained from her face. Jo told Mona she had just been to see her daughter Hannah at the maternity hospital in nearby in Oxford Street. 'Oh, it's probably nothing, Jo,' Mona said soothingly.

But Jo was having none of it. 'Come on!' she said to Debbie, already heading for the door. 'I'll catch up with you some other time, Mona!' she shouted back, as she left the Belvedere.

So agitated were they, that both mother and daughter narrowly missed being hit by a bus on Myrtle Street as they dashed across the road with just one thought on their minds. Jo had always been superstitious, and Mona's comment about the apparition had turned her into a nervous wreck. Finally they reached the hospital and ran up to the ward where Hannah was being monitored. Her bed was empty. Jo grabbed the arm of a young nurse and asked, 'Where's my daughter? Where's she gone?'

'Is she in this ward?' asked the nurse, startled by the rough manner in which Jo had grabbed her.

'She was … but she isn't now! She was in that bed over there!'

The nurse said she'd go and find out, and a few seconds after she had disappeared round the corner of the corridor, Hannah appeared. She waddled out of the toilets, her hands resting on her swollen stomach. When she saw her mother and sister, she shot them a puzzled look. 'What are you two doing here again? she asked. 'Is everything alright?'

'Oh God! Oh thank goodness! I thought something had happened to you!' said Jo, and she gratefully hugged her pregnant daughter.

'Mum, what's up with you? You're in a right state,' said Hannah, and she looked to Debbie, who was blinking rapidly – something she always did when she was nervous – for an explanation for this sudden burst of emotion.

'Oh, nothing, love … we just wondered why your bed was empty, and er …' Jo became stuck for words, not wishing to cause Hannah any alarm. She helped her back into the bed, and then with a slight shake of the head indicated to Debbie that she was to say nothing about the incident in the Belvedere.

Later that evening, at around 11.40pm, Jo was lying in bed with her husband Roy at their home off Holt Road, and was just falling asleep, when Roy started to snore, which instantly woke her up again. She turned away from him, and looked towards the window. Rain had begun to patter gently on the window panes, and this sound somehow helped Jo to start drifting off again into a much-needed sleep, but then she suddenly kicked her leg with an involuntary spasm – something which happened to her from time to time – usually when she was overtired. Frustratingly, she was now wide awake again and staring at the window. And there, coming through that window, was the same red-haired baby she

153

and Debbie had seen at the Belvedere earlier that day. She froze, and her right arm reached back to find Roy's arm under the blankets. She shook him, but he continued to snore, oblivious to everything.

The nebulous baby meanwhile, drifted down towards Jo, and came to a halt about three feet away from her. She could see the smiling face, and this time the baby began to suck his thumb. Jo noticed what looked like a thin string of faint light that led from the baby's navel up into the air, where it seemed to stretch out of the window.

'Who are you, hey?' Jo asked gently, suddenly feeling that the unearthly child posed no threat, and she lifted her head slowly from the pillow and reached out to touch the faintly glowing baby's hand, but before she could reach the little hand, husband Roy awoke with a loud spluttering cough and turned over towards his wife. The baby faded away before Jo's eyes as Roy muttered, 'Were you shaking me before?'

Jo just said, 'No, you must have been dreaming, love. Go back to sleep.' Roy needed no encouragement and was soon snoring again, albeit more quietly. Jo lay there in the darkness, wondering if the mysterious phantom child would return, and she eventually fell asleep as the rain, which had grown heavier driven by the March winds, hammered at the windows.

Three days later, Hannah went into labour, and at 9pm she gave birth to a baby boy – with a full head of red hair. The child's grandfather had red hair, so the baby must have inherited that hair-colour gene from him. The child was named Andrew, and as soon as Jo saw him, she recognised him straight away as the 'ghost' she had seen on two occasions, though she was at a loss to explain how, or why, she had been able to see Andrew before he was born. Whatever the reason, she felt she had been enormously privileged to have met her grandson before he was even born.

Today, we can see clear images of a baby's face before it is born thanks to major advances in ultrasonic computer-scan imaging, but in the early 1980s such a concept was undreamt of. I believe that Andrew was somehow able to astrally project himself out of his mother's womb as she lay in Oxford Street maternity hospital. I believe that Andrew might be an 'old soul' who was possibly the reincarnation of someone who had known Jo in her younger days, and so Andrew felt drawn to his Nan's aura. Strangely enough, there is an extremely strong bond of love between Andrew and his grandmother Jo, even today.

Experiments in hypnotic regression have indicated that some people are able to recall being inside their mother's womb. They remember the sensation of being sometimes upside down, and of hearing their mother's heartbeat and other sounds filtering in from the world outside the womb; almost like being in a sensory-deprivation tank.

Whenever Jo passes the Belvedere Pub or pays the occasional visit to the place, she often thinks of the day she was visited by her unborn grandson.

Street Angel – House Devil

Further back in time, the Belvedere pub has been the backdrop to several other mysteries of the paranormal.

In the 1920s the pub was run by Bill Lawton, who was something of a radio enthusiast. In his spare time he had built a primitive 'cat's whisker' crystal radio set, and had strung an aerial wire from the parlour of the pub and out of a back window, and tied it to a chimney stack. The reception was fair, and Bill could faintly hear the tinny-sounding broadcaster's plummy voice, but only if he wore headphones, as the crystal set did not use any electrical supply; it was powered up solely by the output of the radio energy transmitted by the nearest station. In this case, the station was 6LV, which had been broadcasting to Liverpool since June, 1924.

Bill Lawton decided to splash out a considerable amount of his hard-earned money to purchase a Pye state-of-the-art two-valve radio, which could power up a loudspeaker, thus allowing more than one person to listen to the programmes being transmitted – and that would surely be a draw to the drinkers at the Belvedere.

Well, Bill Lawton had the radio set installed behind the counter in the parlour, atop a table that had been especially bought for the job and would serve as a pedestal. The battery was soon connected, and the set switched on. It took a few seconds for its thermionic valves to 'warm up' – and then a dozen drinkers leaned on the counter, ears pricked, fascinated by the device. They all watched expectantly as Bill twiddled the tuning dial. There was a hiss and then lots of atmospheric whistles and howls, and many chattering voices in foreign tongues. And then Liverpool's own station – 6LV – came through the loudspeaker loud and clear on the 315 metres band. The sounds of the station's Pianoforte Quartet, featuring the young local soprano Miss Annie Wilson, came drifting out of the conical cardboard speaker. All the drinkers were very impressed and smiled their appreciation. 'How about a waltz?' hollered an old man from a far corner of the parlour, perhaps thinking that the musicians on the wireless could hear him and respond to his request.

Billy soon tired of the soprano and turned the dial to hear a rousing brass band broadcasting from the Manchester radio station 2ZY. Everyone cheered, but Bill waved at the drinkers, signalling for them to be quiet, and once again turned the dial. This time a distinctive South Yorkshire accent broke through, and straight away, one of the older drinkers correctly identified the speaker as a Sheffield man. The dial turned again and the melodious voice of a Welsh announcer made everyone laugh. Everyone loved this amazing new toy.

The news of Lawton's radio brought in a few extra drinkers at first, but soon their curiosity began to wane, and many parched customers on a sultry summer evening complained that Bill was spending more time listening to voices from as far away as Barcelona, Berlin and Dublin than to the voices of his regulars crying out for beer.

A few weeks after the radio had become another part of the pub furniture, something very strange took place. A part-time barmaid named Phoebe was serving at the pub one quiet mid-week evening, when one of the drinkers, a man in his thirties named Stan Collins, climbed over the bar and switched on the radio. Bill Lawton was away visiting a relative at the time, and not due back at the pub for another few hours. Stan clicked his fingers in time to the music as the Garner-Schozfield Dance Band played a lively tune, and persuaded Phoebe to do an impromptu foxtrot with him. The five drinkers present laughed at the antics of the young couple, but then, the music faded, and the two-valve Pye radio

157

became quiet, except for a few clicks of static. Then came a well-spoken voice: 'Ah! Stan Collins ... street angel ... house devil!'

Stan Collins let go of Phoebe's arm and stared at the radio in shock, and everyone present, including the barmaid, slowly turned to look at the astonished young man. 'Hey! He just said your name!' Phoebe said to Stan, as if he hadn't heard it himself.

'Who said that then?' said a red-faced Stan, surveying the other drinkers as if he thought one of them had somehow thrown his voice into the radio.

'I said it, Stan,' said the rich accentless voice on the radio. 'The truth is a ghost that scares many.'

All eyes in the parlour were now trained on the radio. All ears primed for more pronouncements.

Stan angrily marched towards the wireless, intending to switch it off.

'If you switch me off, they'll never know what you did, Stan,' said the enigmatic voice.

Stan was perspiring heavily now, and it had nothing to do with it being a close summer evening, for it was relatively cool inside the pub. It was obvious that the voice was making him very nervous; whoever and whatever it was, it had something on the young man, something he did not want others to know.

Click! Before anyone could stop him, Stan had switched the radio off, but Phoebe said, 'What's going on, Stan? Is this some kind of joke you're playing?'

'What did he mean ... house devil ...? Now we'll never know what you did,' complained one of the drinkers, but his words fell on deaf ears, for Stan Collins had already walked out of the Belvedere pub and never returned. He was seen a week later at Southport, and after that, no one ever set eyes on Collins or heard from him again. Rumours circulated Liverpool; Collins had murdered his own grandmother after she had told him she had left him a fortune in her will; Collins was a pervert who had married a man in secret in a ceremony officiated by a homosexual priest ... and so on, but no one ever discovered the truth, though his accuser was said to have been heard several more times on that radio set in the Belvedere pub.

The voice also allegedly disclosed another regular drinker as a bigamist, and even predicted World War Two. The pub landlord Bill Lawton was convinced that the voice was the work of some sophisticated egg-headed prankster, and almost came to blows with a college professor who frequented the pub on a regular basis, but it's unlikely that anyone in those days would have had the technical know-how to make amplitude modulation transmissions and be able to listen, and respond to, the hoax-victim's responses, unless of course, two people were involved, with one person transmitting, from say the back of a van parked outside the pub, and the accomplice somehow passing the responses from the victim to his partner with gestures. It would have meant resorting to extraordinary lengths just to perpetrate such a hoax.

Not long after the outbreak of the Second World War, a 'ghost voice' – as it was nicknamed by the press – began to plague BBC programmes to the forces, and its origin was never traced. In October 1940, the BBC reported that a strange but well-spoken voice had been butting into broadcasts to the troops, uttering inane comments. The signals seemed to be coming from Italy, and sometimes the speaker would speak with an Italian accent, saying such things as: 'Pardi speaking. Can you increase the volume?'

The bothersome voice then started to interrupt Nazi broadcasts, and by July 1944 it was thought to be the work of British Intelligence, but years after the war, intelligence chiefs denied that the ghost voice had anything to do with them. In the summer of 1944, the voice continually contradicted the announcer of the German Overseas programme. When the announcer stated that the Russians had been stopped west of Grodno, the ghost voice broke in, shouting, 'Not true!'

Later, when the German announcer stated that the Russian troops had been thrown back near Dvinsk, the mysterious voice interrupted with: "No, Dvinsk has fallen!"

When the German Overseas radio service broadcast to Asia and Africa days later, the mischievous voice was at work once again. When the announcer spoke of an attempt on Hitler's life, the well-spoken British-sounding voice shouted, 'Hitler must go!' and in the end, the German broadcaster admitted defeat and a marching military band was played at full volume in an effort to drown out the voice.

Of course, from 18 September 1939, up until 30 April 1945, many people in the UK, including Liverpool, tuned their radios to the Nazi propaganda show, *Germany Calling* – fronted by Lord Haw Haw, the nickname of one William Joyce, an American-born fascist politician turned Nazi propagandist. Joyce's broadcasts to Britain on medium wave (and the US on short wave) were intended to demoralise and scare listeners by creating the impression that Joyce knew in great detail what was going on in their very neighbourhoods. He would also exaggerate the numbers of British and American deaths and casualties sustained in the war. On one occasion, Joyce told Liverpool listeners that the Luftwaffe was about to converge on the city, and that the Liver Birds would be brought down so they could 'have a drink in the Mersey'.

Could the voice that was heard on the Belvedere's Pye wireless set in the 1920s have been someone in the military conducting a psychology test on unsuspecting drinkers? If so, why weren't the broadcasts heard on other radios? Or was the eerie speaker an early example of EVP – electronic voice phenomena – where spirits are said to imprint their disembodied voices on tape and solid-state recording devices? We may know more one day.

The Buttercup Man

The third paranormal tale connected to the Belvedere pub concerns a mysterious gentleman who seemed hell-bent on trying to kill people, particularly children. This sinister character first set foot in the Belvedere around the year 1895, when the pub was being managed by two brothers, John and Alfred Martin.

One summer afternoon, a strangely dressed man came into the pub wearing what looked like an old acorn-brown smock, of the type that farmers used to wear, and upon the head of the stranger there was a peculiar black cone-shaped hat with a feather in it, and this tall hat added to the apparent height of the customer, who must have been around six feet anyway. From under this hat, a woolly mass of grey hair protruded, and this, together with the man's large aquiline nose and prominent front teeth, lent him a very distinctive look indeed. He also had a small pair of shifty blue eyes, and a few of the drinkers present noted how the man had the unusual habit of sniffing loudly at the end of each spoken sentence.

The stranger asked for a glass of dandelion wine, but the landlord John Martin said he didn't have any, so the man then requested a flagon of sarsaparilla, and he sat in the corner sipping the sweet flavoured drink as his pinhole eyes shiftily scanned the five or six drinkers scattered around the place.

'May I ask where are you from, sir?' asked an old man leaning at the counter and sucking on a clay pipe that dangled out of the side of his mouth.

'I'm from Caton originally, up near Lancaster, but I've been down here looking for work,' said the stranger, and he suddenly produced a small green bag from his pocket and emptied its contents on to the table in front of him. The drinkers and the landlord couldn't believe their eyes as they watched about twenty or thirty buttercups being tipped out on to the table. The stranger smirked as he began to tie the stalks of the little yellow flowers together until he had made a ring of them. 'They call me the Buttercup Man,' he said, and he arranged the chain of buttercups around the rim of his hat.

'So go on, what's your real name then, Buttercup Man?' asked the pipe-puffing oldster at the counter, fascinated by this new arrival. In all of his years he knew only too well that all human life was to be found in taverns and it made a welcome change in his local to see a new face instead of just the regulars.

'Cow,' replied the Buttercup Man, and he sniffed loudly, and then smiled. 'Toby Cow; it's a silly name, I know, but it's my name all the same.'

Upon hearing a mention of the surname Cow, another elderly drinker named Joe Sewell, his suspicions aroused, quickly turned round to get a better look at the eccentric looking newcomer. Sewell cast his mind back about fifteen years, and realised his suspicions were correct – it was him. Cow had been knocking around in Newsham Park in the summer of 1880, talking to children, crowning little girls with buttercup tiaras and telling them tales to entice them to eat the flowers – and buttercups were poisonous, although most people are not aware of this. Sewell clearly recalled Cow holding a buttercup under the chin of a girl of about five years of age, and all of the similarly aged children around her were fascinated by the golden-yellow glow reflected by the flower on to the girl's neck, which, according to Cow, meant that she liked butter.

A few days after this, four-year-old Mary Holden, from Pinder Street in Everton, had died in agony – from buttercup poisoning. On hearing of her death, Sewell had rushed to the park to confront Mr Cow, but he was nowhere to be found.

A scarlet speck flew in through the pub door as another drinker came into the pub, and this red fleck settled on the back of Cow's hand. 'Ah, a little ladybird,' said Cow, with a childish look of excitement in his minuscule eyes. 'Let me count your spots and see how long I shall live.'

'So tell us, how long are you going to live, Mr Cow?' asked the old man with the pipe.

'Well over a century,' Cow replied, and he lifted his hand and gently blew the ladybird away. It flew up to the ceiling where it settled on an ornate plaster rose. Cow gazed up at the insect, smiling inanely with his buck teeth on full show and he began to sing: 'Ladybird,

ladybird, fly away home, your house is on fire and your children all roam.'

Joe Sewell sidled over to the landlord John Martin, and whispered in his ear, 'That man there has poisoned children.'

Mr Martin had the utmost respect for Sewell, whom he had known for a number of years, and he beckoned for the old man to follow him upstairs to his private quarters. Sewell did so, and told Martin all about the menacing Mr Cow.

After the death of the child in Newsham Park in July 1880, there was another buttercup poisoning case in Sefton Park in the following summer. Once again, a man matching Cow's description had been seen hanging round the poisoned child, who in this case fortunately recovered, and he was able to tell how a man in strange clothes had told him to chew some buttercups. 'They'll make you strong,' the stranger had told the five-year-old, who had almost died from a heavily ulcerated bowel. After this incident Sewell had spotted Cow in the park and had tried to capture him, but he was too agile and had escaped.

'Are you certain it's him?' John Martin asked.

Sewell nodded vigorously, 'I am entirely satisfied it is him, and he hasn't even tried to adopt a new name to conceal his identity.'

'Yes, but it was fifteen years ago, and if we should go to the police, they would probably say that nothing could be proved at this late stage,' said Mr Martin.

'Well at the very least we could watch him,' suggested Sewell, 'I'll wager he's still up to his old tricks.'

'That's all very well, but I have a business to run, Mr Sewell,' said Mr Martin in an almost apologetic tone,

'I'm afraid I have no time to watch Cow. Perhaps you could watch him with your friend, Mr Briggs?'

'Aye, I'll have a word with him,' Mr Sewell said, intending to pay a visit to his old friend George Briggs, who was a carpenter.

When Mr Martin and old Mr Sewell returned to the pub parlour downstairs, they found Toby Cow chatting – in an unknown language – to a tinker of Romany descent. The pair were laughing and having a rather animated discussion, and a few minutes later, Mr Cow left the pub. Sewell left the pub immediately afterwards and shadowed the suspected child-poisoner as Mr Martin asked the tinker what language he had just been speaking in with Mr Cow. 'Shelta Thari,' said the tinker, 'the oldest tongue of the gypsies. It goes back to the ancient Celtic druids, it does.'

'Is Mr Cow a gypsy then?' Mr Martin wanted to know.

The tinker shook his head, 'Nah, he's not Romany. He said he picked up some of the language because his sister married a gypsy years ago.' The tinker then made a unusual remark. 'Mr Cow has some strange beliefs,' he said, but did not go on to explain what had prompted him to make this remark.

Mr Sewell, meanwhile, managed to follow Toby Cow all the way to his lodgings – a run-down boarding house on Catharine Street. Sewell waited for a while, and then purchased a newspaper from a nearby newsagent, as he thought a broadsheet would be ideal to hide behind whilst waiting for Cow to show himself again. Not long after this, Cow emerged from his lodgings carrying a small wicker basket, and he headed north down Mulberry Street with Sewell trailing him at a distance of about fifty yards. Toby Cow headed towards Abercromby

Park. It was a beautiful hot summer's day, and a nanny was pushing a baby along the path which runs around the perimeter of the green, and here and there in the park, on sun-scorched benches and on the warm grass, several young girls and boys sat in twos and threes.

Cow quickly made a beeline for two smartly dressed girls of about seven years of age, and Sewell sat on a nearby bench and tilted his homburg hat forward so the rim came down past his eyebrows, throwing a shadow over his face. He then unfurled the newspaper and peeped surreptitiously over the top of the pages, but Toby Cow seemed so occupied by the girls he never even looked back to see if he was being watched. Mr Sewell kept watch as Cow sat down next to the girls. He removed his ridiculously tall hat and playfully put it on the head of a blonde-haired girl with golden pigtails, and she giggled. Cow was making all sorts of gestures with his hands – throwing them upwards and making flapping movements like a bird's wings as he chatted to the girls. Then suddenly the girls and Cow jumped to their feet – and began to collect buttercups, of which there were many in that park.

The girls were soon festooned with golden necklaces of the innocent looking flower, and Cow, staying faithful to his old modus operandi, held a buttercup under the chin of the dark-haired girl, who was the taller of the two, and Sewell could hear the miscreant come out with his hackneyed patter: 'Ah! see here, you must love butter then, Mary!'

Then Cow opened his wicker basket and took out a pink gingham cloth, which he spread out on the grass as if perparing for a picnic. He looked around – and Sewell immediately ducked under the pages of his newspaper.

166

When the old man peeped over the top of the pages again, he was alarmed to see Cow taking out a jar containing something yellow; it resembled lemon curd. A second jar was produced from the basket, containing what looked like jam. Slices of bread were produced and two green bottles of lemonade, or perhaps ginger beer. Cow took a knife from the basket, and when the lid of the yellow jar had been removed, he dipped the knife into its contents and spread it thickly on to a slice of bread. He offered it to one of the girls.

'No!' roared Sewell, and he rose from the bench, threw down the broadsheet, and tried to run towards the 'Buttercup Man'. Taken completely by surprise in his devilish work, Cow spun round and leapt to his feet. He picked up the jar – and threw it with great force at Sewell. The jar's contents splattered all over the old man's suit and bounced off his homburg. Toby Cow then ran off and exited the park. He was seen to run in the direction of Bedford Street North.

Sewell attracted the attention of a policeman walking up Oxford Street on his beat, and told him what had happened, and the officer of the law immediately went in search of Cow, but failed to find him, so he and another constable called at Cow's lodging house, and waited there, but the would-be poisoner never returned to pick up his few belongings.

The yellow substance in the jar was found to be butter laced with buttercups, and the other jar had contained damson jam – which would have no doubt masked the bitter taste of the buttercup's poison.

The tinker who had spoken to Toby Cow in his native tongue, Shelta Thari, said that Cow had told him that long ago, a cult had existed in Lancashire which had sacrificed children in the summer months to the Flower of the Sun – what we now know as the buttercup. The sacrifices were made to ensure a good harvest and to thank the sun for the gift of summer. Even today, on Mayday, some Irish farmers still rub buttercups on the udders of their cows, because they believe the 'sacred flower' can encourage milk production.

Two years later, John Martin was reading a newspaper, when he noticed some very disturbing news. In June 1897, a boy named William Foxcroft, aged just four years, had died after eating buttercups. This incident had happened in Caton, Lancashire – the very village from which Toby Cow had hailed. There were rumours that the Buttercup Man had been up to his old tricks again, but the mystery deepened when the news reached the Belvedere pub that Toby Cow had died of a fever in 1896.

Mr Sewell was walking with a lady friend through Abercromby Park at noon on a beautiful August day that year, when he came across Toby Cow once more, standing near a group of children, on the eastern side of the park, close to St Catherine's Church. Sewell couldn't believe his eyes, and he turned to his female companion and pointed to Cow, asking, 'Tell me, do you see a man in a tall hat over there?' Sewell's friend said she could see only children playing, and when Sewell glanced back at the knot of children, he saw that Toby Cow had vanished.

For years, and always in the summer months, Cow's ghost was said to frequent the Belvedere, the nearby Blackburne Arms, and several parks across the city.

THE EMPIRE
Hanover Street

Peggalow

When I was a child, my grandmother Rose Slemen would often captivate me with intriguing tales as I sat with her round the fire at her old home off Myrtle Street. Gran was a font of fascinating and often scary stories, and she introduced me, via her storytelling, to such legendary characters as Spring-Heeled Jack and Peggalow. 'Who?' you might ask on hearing the latter. Well the story I am about to relate was told to me by my grandmother, and at the time I assumed it was all make-believe, but many years later, I was talking to a middle-aged woman in a cake shop, of all places, and somehow we got talking about ghosts and strange goings on, when she astounded me by saying, 'It's a wonder you haven't mentioned Peggalow in your books.'

'Ah, so you heard about him too then?' I replied, and she nodded with a smile, and recounted to me almost word for word what I had heard all those years ago.

Years afterwards, I was at a book-signing event in Cheshire, when an old man asked me to sign a book he was buying for his wife. Then he leaned forward on the table and said, rather conspiratorially: 'Have you ever heard a story about a little man named Peggalow ... or possibly Pigloo?'

I nodded, and asked my elderly fan to tell his version, and again it was almost word for word what I had heard when I was just a boy of seven or eight. The old man's name was John Singleton, and he said his wife was related to the Alice Jones mentioned in the story. Without more ado, here is the tale.

Around the year 1895, Fred Vinall was the landlord of the Empire pub on Hanover Street, and one rainy night, a mysterious friend of his, a foreigner named Marigotti, called at the tavern in a dreadful state, with a raging fever, asking Fred if he could stay with him until he felt better. Marigotti had a mahogany chest with him that night, and in private, he confided to Fred Vinall that he had stolen the trunk from a well-to-do person's home in Aigburth, and had found it to contain many peculiar things, as well as odd objects made of gold and silver.

Marigotti was given lodgings at the pub, but his condition worsened and after three days he died from pneumonia, and was buried in a pauper's grave. Fred kept the old trunk his late friend had stolen, and now and then he would take a rummage round in it and try to make sense of the things he found there. He confided in a friend that the chest contained 'things no mortal was supposed to see' and he resolved to get rid of these enigmatic 'things', but seemed too darkly fascinated by the objects to get shut of them.

About a year later, Fred's beautiful young niece, Alice Jones, came to stay at the pub after her mother was hospitalised with consumption. The girl's father had died years before. Bored by the long hours she was forced to spend by herself, Alice went mooching about in the upper rooms of the pub one evening, and came upon the chest of mystery. She opened it and found gold and silver daggers, a crystal ball, books in gobbledygook writing, incomprehensible charts, and several dusty bottles. One globular blue-tinted bottle had a red wax seal on it with a scroll attached, and when Alice wiped the dust from the bottle with her fingers, she saw a little doll of a man in old-fashioned green clothes, pale stockings below his knees, and a white ruffled collar. The three-inch-long doll sat cross-legged with its head bowed, and as Alice squinted in at the figure she suddenly jumped backwards – the figure had sat up and was now looking at her.

The girl shrieked and dropped the bottle, but curiosity drew her back to it. She picked it up and looked at the tiny man inside it. He waved. 'My name is Peggalow,' he announced in a faint but perfectly clear voice. He had long black hair and a Van Dyke beard. He claimed that an evil sorcerer had shrunk him and imprisoned him in the bottle many many years ago, and asked Alice who the current monarch was. 'Victoria, why?' she replied, and Peggalow said that Queen Elizabeth had been on the throne when he was confined in the bottle. 'Break that seal up there and I'll come out and tell you more!' the little man yelled, impatiently pointing to the wax seal around the cork.

Alice's instincts told her that Peggalow had been sealed up for a reason, and she firmly shook her head. Peggalow knelt on the floor of the bottle and in a meek little voice said, 'Please, I beg of you!'

But Alice still refused to break the seal, and so Peggalow asked, 'If I grant you a wish will you break the seal?'

Now more interested, Alice said, 'Perhaps,' and Peggalow carefully instructed her as to what she must do. At midnight she was to recite a long spell by candlelight as she faced the old mirror in the room. The first words of the magical spell were: 'Nema live morf su reviled tub noitatpmet otni ..." and as Alice carefully wrote the words down, Peggalow recited more and more of these incomprehensible words.

'You shall have anything you desire, my Alice! Love, happiness, the riches of the world!' promised the tiny bottled man. At midnight, as the pub clock struck twelve, the spell was recited in the upstairs room by the light of a single candle, but Alice fled when a terrifying grinning face appeared in the mirror, and something or someone touched her left shoulder. She ran terrified into the parlour, crying hysterically, and confessed to Uncle Fred what she had done, and he and a few of the late drinkers rushed up to the room in time to see the mahogany chest shaking on the floor. Fred Vinall slammed the chest shut and fetched the family bible and a crucifix, which he tied to the chest, and immediately it stopped shaking.

The 'spell' dictated to gullible Alice by the sinister Peggalow was simply the Lord's Prayer spoken backwards – a supposedly sure way of conjuring up

Beelzebub when recited between midnight and one in the morning. Fred Vinall arranged for the chest to be thrown in a midden, but a sailor salvaged it. The remains of that sailor were said to have been buried at sea when he was mysteriously burnt to a crisp in his bunk on a ship bound from Liverpool to New York. The sailor's bedding and pillowcase were untouched, and yet the fire had reduced his bones to ash, which sounds like the baffling phenomenon known as spontaneous human combustion. Today the whereabouts of the mahogany chest, and the bottled entity Peggalow are unknown.

THE NEWINGTON
Upper Newington

The Spinning Parlour

Most rooms spin after you've had a bit too much to drink, but in 1900 there was a strange case of a spinning pub parlour which could not be explained by anyone's over-indulgence in the demon drink. This inexplicable incident took place one evening in February 1900 in the Newington public house, which is still open to date and situated on the corner of Renshaw Street and the once busy thoroughfare from which the drinking establishment lends its name – Upper Newington.

The pub landlord of the day, John Harrison, was alerted by the sound of heavy thumping coming from underneath the floor of the parlour, on this particularly cold February evening at 10.10pm, and so he hurried down the steps to the cellar carrying an oil lamp to see if anything was amiss. Harrison could find nothing to account for the loud bumps, which only he had detected via the soles of his shoes. He went back upstairs and was in the middle of serving a customer when he first heard a low rumbling sound, followed by a vibrating sensation under his feet. There were only six drinkers in the parlour that evening, far fewer than normal, possibly on account of the thick snow outside, which was probably keeping most of the regulars at home. The six drinkers and Harrison's three barmen also felt and heard the seemingly seismic disturbance this time.

A few minutes later, the last orders bell jangled and bottles and glasses rattled as the whole parlour shook. Everyone present believed that an earthquake had struck, but then something spectacularly bizarre took place: the parlour began to slowly rotate. An old drinker was flung back against the wall by the centrifugal forces as the rotation increased in speed. A hat stand toppled over, glasses slid off tables, and the gas mantles in the wall lamps flickered. The room was spinning anti-clockwise, and a Mrs Elizabeth Charnock, a beerseller from Knotty Ash who was related to Mr Harrison's wife, was thrown screaming to the floor and suffered a fit.

After about a minute the room stopped spinning and the gas-lamps brightened to normal luminosity again. A few of the drinkers felt quite giddy and staggered for the door to throw up outside. One or two of people in the bar had not even been aware of the spinning parlour, which only deepened the mystery. The drink was blamed, but others were convinced that the whole uncanny incident had been some kind of warped joke of the Devil.

Rational reasons, however elaborate, cannot begin to explain the spinning parlour of the Newington, but perhaps the phenomenon was something to do with a vortex or some dimensional disturbance within space and time. I have documented such suspected cases of a space-time disturbance in my books before, in particular, when I detailed the curious case of the hole which opened up in the floor of a room of the Victoria Hotel, Bristol, in the early hours of 9 December 1873.

An off-duty soldier from Leeds, Thomas B Cumpston, and his Liverpool-born wife Ann Martha, had been sleeping soundly in their room at the hotel, when, at about one in the morning, Mrs Tongue, the hotel manager, heard excited voices coming from their room, and went to investigate. The couple said they had heard strange noises and voices in the room, and believed it to be haunted. Mrs Tongue pacified the couple and convinced them that they had both had a nightmare and somehow persuaded them to return to their bed.

At four in the morning, Mrs Tongue was startled from her slumbers by gunshots and loud screams of murder coming from the room where the Cumpstons were lodging. She put on her night-gown, lit an oil lamp and hurried in her bare feet to the room to see what the matter was this time. Outside the door, Mrs Tongue heard Mrs Cumpston exclaim: 'Keep that knife away from me!'

The hotel manager burst into the dark room and found Mr and Mrs Cumpston hastily exiting the window in their nightclothes. They dropped a full twelve feet and rushed barefooted to the railway station, where they told the night superintendent, a Thomas Harker, an incredible story as he sat drinking his cocoa in the booking office.

Mr Cumpston said he and his wife had just escaped from a den of thieves and had almost been waylaid by them. Now Mr Cumpston feared the blackguards would follow him to the station. Mr Harker took the couple into the parcel office and settled them by the fire, then in a calm voice asked them to go through the story again. Mrs Cumpston said her husband had got out of bed after feeling it 'open up'. A black hole soon opened in the mattress. She tried to pull him up as she heard echoing voices crying out from below.

'My husband has a revolver, and he fired at them!' Mrs Cumpston said, and Mr Harker asked Thomas Cumpston if this was true. 'Yes, I'm a soldier,' he replied, and produced the revolver. He said that he and his wife had leapt out of the haunted bed only to find that another hole opened up in the carpet. In his terror, Mr Cumpston tripped and fell down the hole, where he heard screeching voices. By acting quickly and summoning up all her strength, his wife had somehow pulled him out of the hole.

As soon as he was out he grabbed his service revolver and fired first into the ceiling to warn whoever was lurking in the hole, and then he fired several shots at the people down in the abyss, before instructing his wife to get out of the room by jumping from the bed over to the windowsill. They then opened the window and escaped from the room by dropping on to the pavement below. The voices could still be heard at the window above, so Mr Cumpston, on the advice from his hysterical wife, fired another shot at the window, and only then had they run off for help.

Mrs Tongue meanwhile, left her hotel in search of a policeman to report the bizarre behaviour of the Cumpstons and the gunshots, and she encountered Police

Constable 310 on his beat at Bath Parade. She informed him of Cumpston's antics and told him how the couple had headed for the railway station. The policeman went straight there and found the Cumpstons seated comfortably before the fire in the parcel office with Harker. After listening to their seemingly far-fetched tale, the policeman argued that the Victoria Hotel was a respectable establishment, and not likely to be the place where a den of thieves might choose to operate, but nevertheless, he paid a visit to the room the Cumpstons had vacated but found no bullet holes; only the blankets of the bed were in disarray. The entire incident was 'explained' away as a collective hallucination, shared by Mr and Mrs Cumpston.

Here in Liverpool, there was a similar unexplained distortion of time and space within the Wellington Rooms, the former home of the Irish Centre on Mount Pleasant. This incident took place one afternoon in the late 1970s, when the Irish Centre was closed. Two painters were decorating a hall in the building when they saw one of the walls move towards them as a low rumbling sound filled the room. The painters dropped their brushes and ran into another room to tell a member of staff what had taken place, but when he followed them into the hall he found the wall in question completely intact and still in its normal position. The fumes from the paint were thought to have caused the painters to hallucinate, even though, being professional workmen, they had ventilated the hall and had never experienced any hallucinogenic effects from their paint before.

To add to the mystery, another person who was working in the Irish Centre at the same time, later reported that he too had heard the rumbling sound, just as the painters had described.

Seeing Double

From 1897 to around 1920, an original but unsigned oil painting hung on the walls of the Newington's bar, and the subject of this painting was a rather unremarkable scene of a jolly round-faced rosy-cheeked publican standing with his arms folded behind the bar of a pub with an ornate gold-framed mirror behind him and the usual rows of bottled wines and spirits on either side of the grand looking glass.

The owner of the Newington around 1905 was a Mr Matty Walling, and his wife didn't care too much for the painting, as it had acquired a sticky yellowish patina over the years because of cigarette, pipe and cigar smoke, so she asked Matty to remove it. He said he was happy to remove it once she could find a better picture to replace it. And so one day in the autumn of 1904, whilst the couple were out shopping in Bootle, Mrs Walling spotted a beautiful oil painting of roses arranged in a vase, and her husband purchased it. Now at last Mrs Walling had found the painting that would replace the grubby one of the moon-faced publican on the wall of their pub.

Since it was their day off, the Wallings then decided to call into the Jawbone Tavern, Bootle's oldest pub, on Litherland Road, for a little refreshment – and the couple received the shock of their lives, for there, behind the bar, was the very man who featured in that grimy oil painting back at the Newington pub. He had a round jovial face, rose-red cheeks, and there too behind him was the distinctive gold-framed mirror with the shelves of spirits and wines arranged on either side. But then came the second shock. When the couple had ordered their drinks

179

and settled themselves down at a table in the Jawbone, Mr Walling tapped his wife on the shoulder and drew her attention to another oil painting hanging on the wall just above her head. It featured an all too familiar scene – the unmistakable interior of the Newington's bar!

The manager of the pub couldn't remember how long the oil painting of the Newington had been displayed on the wall, and he laughed heartily when Mrs Walling informed him that his own portrait had been hanging on the walls of her own pub on Renshaw Street in Liverpool ever since they had taken over the licence.

'Well I've been here for quite a few years,' said the publican, 'more than I care to mention,' and he generously treated the couple to a few drinks on the house.

A fortnight later, Matty Walling took the painting down from the wall of the Newington and made his way up to the Jawbone Tavern to show it to the publican – but when he arrived at the Bootle pub, Matty was told that no publican matching the man he had described had ever worked in the tavern. Matty Walling thought this was some kind of practical joke, but the present publican came down to see the Newington's landlord and sternly told him that he had been the manager of the pub for five years and knew of no round-faced employee of the type described. Mr Walling slowly realised that he and his wife must have encountered a ghost two weeks before. It was the only possible explanation. The peculiar connection between the Newington and the Jawbone Tavern via the peculiar paintings was never satisfactorily explained.

THE CHILDWALL ABBEY
Childwall Abbey Road

Mad Scientist or Genius

According to scientists, life on earth began around four thousand million years ago when the world was a young, but utterly forbidding planet. The turbulent atmosphere in those times was made up of a mixture of steam, nitrogen, methane, ammonia, carbon and many other gases. But one very important gas was absent: oxygen. This gas is produced by plant life and did not exist in a free state before the arrival of life, but then how exactly, did life on earth begin? Well, established science holds that life came into being in an entirely accidental way.

The dead matter floating about in the 'oceans' of the

early earth supposedly consisted of various random molecules that collided with one another, and one day, a specific molecule was formed in this random way which could reproduce copies of itself. But there are problems with this theory. Protein chains – organic compounds containing the elements carbon, hydrogen, oxygen and nitrogen – consist of sub-units called amino acids, and there are twenty possibilities for each link in the protein chain.

The French biophysicist Lecomte de Nouy has calculated that if a new combination were tried every millionth of a second, it would take a period longer than the life of the earth to form the right type of protein chain! Nevertheless, scientists are adamant about the theory of life beginning in the world's primeval ocean-soup.

In 1952 it occurred to an American graduate student, Stanley Lloyd Miller, that an experiment to reproduce the environment conducive to life in primordial times could be set up in the laboratory. He put methane, ammonia, hydrogen and water in a flask and boiled the contents for days, occasionally discharging some artificial lightning (via two electrodes) through the mixture to simulate the ultraviolet radiation of the sun. Miller observed that the mixture in the flask quickly darkened. After a week, he analysed the solution that had formed in the flask and found that, in addition to rudimentary substances lacking in nitrogen atoms, he had glycine and alanine, two simple amino acids. He also found minute traces of more complicated amino acids.

Miller was surprised at the compounds forming so quickly and in such large quantities. In the mere space of a week, one-sixth of the methane in the flask had produced such startling compounds. The fact that Miller had created the building blocks of life in a laboratory generated shockwaves that elated the scientific community and in equal measure upset the religious authorities. One hundred and fifteen years before Miller's experiment, fifty-three-year-old Englishman Andrew Crosse carried out a similar experiment. Crosse's efforts allegedly produced no mere amino acids, but the formation of a totally new type of insect.

Andrew Crosse was born into a wealthy family on 17 June 1784. He was a child prodigy who had mastered Ancient Greek by the age of eight. When Crosse was nine he was sent to Dr Seyer's School at Bristol, where he was captivated by the subject of science and around the age of twelve, he became obsessed with the new science of electricity.

Young Crosse was a notorious joker, and often wired up the metal doorknobs of the classroom to a huge accumulator, in order to give the teachers an electric shock whenever they entered the class. Electricity was to become a lifetime obsession, and when Crosse inherited the family estates and fortune upon the death of his mother in 1805, the young science buff used a substantial amount of his newly-acquired wealth to set up a well-equipped laboratory at Fyne Court, his family seat, where he was to perform a series of bizarre experiments.

The isolated country mansion of Fyne Court, in the Quantock Hills of Somerset, gained an eerie reputation, thanks to Crosse. The locals were sure he was an evil wizard, because of the way he captured the powers of lightning by conducting the bolts through a network of copper cables (over a mile in length) that radiated from the Fyne Court laboratory like a gigantic web. Whenever a storm raged over the Quantock Hills, the superstitious locals would watch the forks of lightning dancing about on the copper cables.

To the Somerset yokels, Squire Crosse had to be in league with the Devil in order to be capable of attracting the lightning, but unknown to them, Crosse was tapping the huge voltages from the lightning flashes to power his electrical experiments. Crosse was intrigued by the various types of crystal that are formed when an electrical current is passed through certain mineral solutions. The outcomes of this pioneering experimental work were all written up in a notebook. In 1837, this notebook recorded a dramatic incident that has never been explained. The entry reads:

> *In the course of my endeavours to form artificial minerals by a long continued electric action on fluids, holding in solution such substances as were necessary to my purpose, I had recourse to every variety of contrivance that I could think of; amongst others I constructed a wooden frame, which supported a Wedgewood funnel, within which rested a quart basin on a circular piece of mahogany. When this basin was filled with a fluid, a strip of flannel wetted with the same was suspended over the side of the basin and inside the funnel, which, acting as a syphon, conveyed the fluid out of the basin through the funnel in successive drops: these drops fell into a smaller funnel of glass placed beneath the other, and which contained a piece of somewhat porous red oxide from Vesuvius. This stone was kept constantly electrified.*
> *On the fourteenth day from the commencement of this experiment, I observed through the lens a few small whitish excrescences, or nipples, projecting from about the middle of the electrified stone. On the eighteenth*

day these projections enlarged, and stuck out seven or eight filaments, each of them longer than the hemisphere on which they grew. On the twenty-sixth day these appearances assumed the form of a perfect insect, standing erect on a few bristles which formed its tail.

On the twenty-eighth day these little creatures moved their legs ... After a few days they detached themselves from the stone, and moved about at pleasure.

Crosse was obviously amazed at the incredible outcome of his experiment, and he tried in vain to find a rational explanation that would account for the appearance of the strange insect. He immediately repeated the experiment and again recorded the outcome in his notebook:

After many months' action and consequent formation of certain crystalline matters, I observed similar excrescences with those before described at the edge of the fluid in every one of the cylinders except two, which contained the carbonate of potassa and the metalic arsenic; and in due time the whitish appearances were developed into insects. In my first experiment I had made use of flannel, wood, and a volcanic stone. In the last, none of these substances were present.

But Crosse could still not accept what he was seeing. The existence of the new mites – or acari, as they are called – seemed to run contrary to the laws of biology. Crosse was determined to get to the bottom of the mite mystery, so he carried out the experiment yet again, and later wrote:

I had omitted to insert within the bulb of the retort a resting place for these acari (they are always destroyed if they fall back into the fluid from which they have emerged). It is strange that, in a solution eminently caustic and under an atmosphere of oxihydrogen gas, one single acarus should have made its appearance.

Crosse wrote a detailed report of his bizarre discovery and sent it to the Electrical Society in London. Although the report was sceptically received, W H Weeks, a respected experimenter, was chosen by the Electrical Society to repeat the Crosse experiment.

Weeks proved to be much more careful than Crosse at setting up the experiment. He thoroughly sterilised all of the lab equipment and worked under stringent quarantine-like conditions. News of the Crosse experiment broke as Weeks worked. A newspaper in the west of England published an account it, and soon the news agencies of Britain and the rest of Europe were running the story. Then the results of the Weeks experiment were announced; Weeks too had produced the strange insects.

The reclusive Crosse suddenly found himself in the eye of a hurricane of unwanted publicity. The mites he had created were named Acarus Crossii in his honour, and the creator-scientist was hailed as a genius by many of his colleagues. But the religious authorities and the ignorant hoi polloi were outraged by the 'blaspheming' Crosse. They saw him as a meddling devil who had set himself up as a rival to God. When Crosse returned to Fyne Court, the furious locals threw stones at him and killed his livestock. On several occasions the dullards even set fire to his crops, and the local Reverend Philip

186

Smith, who incited much of the trouble, even conducted a service of exorcism on Crosse's country estate!

Crosse came to Liverpool on several occasions, the most notable of these visits being a lecture at St George's Hall in September 1854 when the British Association for the Advancement of Science came to the city for their annual meeting. In the jury room of St George's Hall, Crosse delivered a controversial lecture on electricity entitled 'On the Apparent Mechanical Action accompanying Electric Transfer' – in which he explained how electrical impulses could cause motion in both electromagnetic materials and muscle fibres in human and animal bodies.

After the talk, Crosse was invited by several other like-minded scientists to take part in a grisly experiment at the Childwall Abbey Hotel in what was then a remote and leafy suburb of the city. The Childwall Abbey was regularly used as a dead house and for coroner's inquests, but on this occasion, an attempt was made to temporarily resuscitate a hanged murderer using an array of voltaic piles, which were, in effect, crude batteries.

Crosse watched spellbound as wires from the batteries were attached to copper pins which were then beaten with a hammer into the shaved head of the corpse. The pins served as electrodes which penetrated the skull and made contact with the brain of the corpse. When current was applied, the eyes of the dead killer shot open and swivelled from left to right, and the mouth of the corpse opened and closed with a chilling clacking sound.

The scientists conducting the experiment told Crosse that these 'psychogalvanic' experiments had been carried out on the corpses of men, women and children who had died in the local workhouses. The hanged man's corpse

187

was not an ideal subject because the spine, snapped at the top by the noose, would not allow the current to reach the limbs, but the body of a fourteen-year-old boy who had died from a fever had sat up and his vocal chords had even made a moaning sound when current was applied to the brain via several holes drilled in the skull.

The corpse of a twenty-five-year-old woman had made strange facial expressions and grinned, and even stuck its tongue out when parts of the cerebral cortex had been stimulated with low current. Crosse suggested the erection of a lightning conductor above the Childwall Abbey Hotel to feed natural high-tension lightning bolts down a cable into a Leyden Jar, but it is not known if his suggestion was ever taken up.

The grotesque experiments continued for a while until several officials from the Church heard about them and told the landlord of the Childwall pub to stop letting out the premises to the blasphemous scientists. Comparisons were naturally drawn between the research into the reanimation of the dead and the work of the fictional mad-scientist Frankenstein, featured in the sensational 1818 novel by Mary Shelley.

On 6 July 1855, Andrew Crosse died after suffering a paralytic seizure. His last words were, 'The utmost extent of human knowledge is but comparative ignorance.' Even today, scientists cannot explain away the acari that were apparently created by Crosse, and what's more, no scientist is even willing to try and reproduce the fascinating nineteenth century experiment. There had been talk within scientific circles of interfacing the brains of the dead with computers, to see if it were possible to extract memories and perhaps even 'reboot' the brain using computer-coordinated impulses of low-level current into the neuron network.

Such technology may, in theory, make it possible one day to view the memories of a dead person. Forensic experts would be extremely interested in this tool because if the brain of a murdered person could be examined digitally, it could provide access to 'memory footage' of the last things the dead person saw – and that could include visual footage of the murderer killing the victim – from the latter's viewpoint, of course.